JAM JAM JAM

with
70s ROCK

www.jamtrax.com

Exclusive Distributors:
Music Sales Limited
8/9 Frith Street
London W1D 3JB England

Music Sales Pty Limited
120 Rothschild Avenue
Rosebery, NSW 2018
Australia

Order No. AM967428
ISBN: 0-7119-8497-2
This book © Copyright 2001 by Wise Publications

www.musicsales.com

Cover Design by Kim Waller
Music engraved by Cambridge Notation

Printed and bound in Malta.

Your Guarantee of Quality
As publishers we strive to produce every book to the highest commercial standards.
The music has been freshly engraved and the book has been carefully designed to minimise
awkward page turns and to make playing from it a real pleasure.
Particular care has been given to specifying acid-free, neutral-sized paper made from pulps which
have not been elemental chlorine bleached. This pulp is from farmed sustainable forests and was
produced with special regard for the environment.
Throughout, the printing and binding have been planned to ensure a sturdy, attractive publication
which should give years of enjoyment. If your copy fails to meet our high standards, please
inform us and we will gladly replace it.

Music Sales' complete catalogue describes thousands of titles and is available in full colour sections
by subject, direct from Music Sales Limited. Please state your areas of interest and send a
cheque/postal order for £1.50 for postage to:
Music Sales Limited, Newmarket Road, Bury St Edmunds, Suffolk IP33 3YD.

This publication is not authorised for sale in the
United States of America and/or Canada.

Wise Publications
London/New York/Sydney/Paris/Copenhagen/Madrid/Tokyo

CONTENTS

On the CDs

The audio content is split across two CDs and separated into two sections: section 1 (CD1) is the backing tracks minus lead guitar & vocals, while section 2 (CD2) is the backing tracks with all guitar parts added, so in addition to the written tab you can hear the rhythm, fills and solos as they should be played ! (An additional backing track has been included for the slide guitar part of Rocky Mountain Way)

Music produced by Steve Finch.
Music arranged by Steve Allsworth and Paul Bielatowicz.
Recorded at the TOTAL ACCURACY SOUNDHOUSE, Romford, England.
Mastered at Hilton Grove, London, England.
Steve Allsworth and Paul Bielatowicz: guitar.   Mick Ash: bass.
Alison Pearce: keyboards.
Pete Riley: drums.
Road Rock Studios use Line 6 products.

Music transcribed by Steve Allsworth *(songs 3,4,5,6,8)*;
Paul Bielatowicz *(songs 1,7)*; Richard Barrett *(song 2)*.

www.jamtrax.com

INTRODUCTION

The TOTAL ACCURACY 'JAM WITH...' series is a powerful learning tool that will help you extend your stockpile of licks and fills and develop your improvisational skills. The combination of musical notation and guitar tablature in the book, together with backing tracks on the CD, gives you the opportunity to learn each track note for note and then jam with a professional session band. The track listing reflects some of the 70's most popular recordings, providing something for guitarists to have fun with and improvise with, as well as something to aspire to.

Eight tracks on CD1 are full length backing tracks recorded minus lead guitar. (A ninth backing track has been included for the slide guitar part of *Rocky Mountain Way*). The eight tracks on CD2 feature the backing tracks with the lead guitar parts added. Although many of you will have all the original tracks in your own collections, we have provided them in the package for your reference. The 'JAM WITH...' series allows you to accurately recreate the original, or to use the transcriptions in this book in conjunction with the backing tracks as a basis for your own improvisation. For your benefit we have put definite endings on the backing tracks, rather than fading them out as is the case on some of the original recordings. The accompanying transcriptions correspond to our versions. Remember, experimenting with your own ideas is equally important for developing your own style; most important of all, however, is that you enjoy *JAM WITH 70's ROCK* and HAVE FUN!

The 70s saw the birth of hard rock and heavy metal, with songs that fitted into this genre flourishing, in marked contrast to the blues and pop based songs that dominated the charts during the 60s. Guitar in the 70s was about big riffs and energetic soloing, on the cutting edge of a fresh, new sound.

As well as the hard rock American bands such as Steppenwolf and Lynyrd Skynyrd achieving worldwide acclaim, British acts The Who and Black Sabbath were part of a new breed of anti-social musicians who helped to redefine rock music as we know it today. Solo artists such as Joe Walsh and Eric Clapton, with their own brand of blues-based rock also achieved success in an ever changing musical climate, whilst exceptions to the hard rock trend - Boston - helped to redefine the sound of the guitar.

Boston was formed by guitarist Tom Scholz in the mid 70s, and joined by Fran Sheehan on bass, Brad Delp on guitar and vocals, Barry Goudreau on guitar, and Sib Hashian on drums. Their first release eventually went on to sell over 16 million albums in the US alone, and spent over two years in the charts.

Two years later the successful formula was repeated with *Don't Look Back* which also topped the charts. Scholz then became embroiled in a lengthy contractual dispute with CBS records and former manager Paul Ahern, but also found the time to develop the famous mini-amplifier Rockman line of products. Goudreau, Hashian and Sheehan had all left by the mid 80s, but Scholz returned with Delp in 1986. *Third Stage* produced two further hits, and sent Boston's total sales to well over 50 million. Scholz eventually won his case against CBS in 1990 but lost out to former band member Ahern. The 90s saw Scholz release *Walk On* without any former members, and although it was a disappointment, it still reached top five.

Joe Walsh began a long and successful career in 1965 with the G-clefs, and after a short stint with a local band, found major success with the James Gang three years later. Walsh began developing an early heavy metal technique, similar to that of guitarist Jeff Beck. In 1972, Walsh formed Barnstorm with Joe Vitale on drums and Kenny Passerelli on bass. The band's self-titled debut showed a lot of promise, but it wasn't until the follow up a year later *The Smoker You Drink, The Player You Get* (despite being credited to Joe) that Walsh achieved gold-selling success.

The band broke up later that year, and Joe went on to guest with Stephen Stills, The Eagles and B.B.King before producing another gold album *So What* in 1975. Later that year, Walsh replaced Bernie Leaden as full-time joint lead guitarist in the Eagles with Glen Frey. His solo on *Hotel California* is probably his most memorable moment. He released further solo albums, *But Seriously Folks...*, *There Goes The Neighbourhood* and *You Bought It - You Name It*, and also contributed to the soundtrack album *Urban Cowboy* in 1980.

His career continued to prosper during the late 80s and 90s as a solo and session player, but more recently he has been filling stadiums again as part of a reformed Eagles.

Formed in 1964 in Jacksonville, Florida, the hard-rocking dixie band Lynyrd Skynyrd took their name from P.E. teacher Leonard Skinner who was famed for his hatred of long haired students. The original line-up included Ronnie Van Zant on vocals, Gary Rossington on guitar, Allen Collins on guitar, Larry Jungstrom on bass and Bob Burns on drums.

After a string of singles and tours of the southern states in the late 60s, the band was eventually signed in 1972 by Al Kooper. Jungstrom was replaced by Leon Wilkeson on bass. The debut *Pronounced Leh-Nerd Skin-Nerd* (1973) also featured former Strawberry Alarm Clock guitarist Ed King and the southern boogie of Billy Powell on keyboards. The three guitar line-up generated much interest, especially when they supported The Who on the Quadrophenia tour, with their anthemic *Free Bird* the highlight. A year later, the band had their biggest hit with *Sweet Home Alabama* (from *Second Helping*) which was a response to Neil Young's criticisms of the south in his songs 'Southern Man' and 'Alabama'.

Ed King became the first victim of the band's excesses with drugs and alcohol when he left in 1975, and Van Zant was regularly in trouble with the law. Steve Gaines replaced Ed King after a series of bust-ups with Van Zant, and Artimus Pyle took over from Burns on the drums. With two more studio albums, *Nothin' Fancy* and *Give Me Back My Bullets*, the band cemented their reputation as a class act on the verge of greatness. Three days after the release of *Street Survivors* in October 1977, the band was decimated in a plane crash, when Van Zant, Gaines and manager Dean Kilpatrick were killed. The band dispersed, but turned up in various guises, until the remaining line-up reformed in 1987 for a one-off tribute concert.

The band still tour and record, and continue to enjoy high record sales.

The Who were formed in Shepherd's Bush in 1964 with Pete Townshend on guitar and vocals, Roger Daltrey on vocals, John Entwistle on bass and later Keith Moon on drums. Dressed stylishly and courting a Mod audience, the band became notorious through Townshend's stage antics which involved instrument mutilation. Their anti-social behaviour didn't attract a major label until Decca helped them release *I Can't Explain* in 1965, which became an anthem for Britain's restless youth. Follow-ups *Anyway Anyhow Anywhere* and *My Generation* encapsulated the frustrations of pilled-up Mods and disposable culture. The latter became the title track of their debut album, which redefined 60s rock.

The band gained popularity throughout the 60s, but didn't embrace the album market fully until the release of the rock opera *Tommy* (1969). It spawned the release of 'Pinball Wizard' and later a successful film. The following album *Who's Next* two years later, included their 70s staple hits 'Baba O'Riley' and 'Won't Get Fooled Again'. Townshend completed work on the concept album *Quadrophenia* in 1973, which was inspired by Mod culture, and although not as accessible as *Tommy*, it became a successful film featuring Toyah and Sting.

The Who emerged after a short hiatus in the 70s with *Who Are You*, but this was overshadowed by the tragic death of Moon in September 1978. The band carried on with Kenny Jones until 1982 when they finally split.

Periodic reunions throughout the 80s included Live Aid and a 25th anniversary tour, as well as an epic *Quadrophenia* live in Hyde Park. The band continues to release masters of previous albums to worldwide acclaim.

Originally known as Earth, and eventually as Black Sabbath in 1969, the Midlands group comprised Terry 'Geezer' Butler on bass, Tony Iommi on guitar, Bill Ward on drums, and Ozzy Osbourne on vocals. The name was partly inspired by a book on the occult by Dennis Wheatley, and a cult horror film of the same name, both of which hint at the band's doom-laden, heavy metal brand of music.

Their self-titled debut in 1970 and *Paranoid* (also 1970) pioneered the sound of heavy metal as we know it today, with scary detuned riffs based on horror films. The latter album produced a single of the same name (arguably one of the most famous Sabbath songs ever) giving the band their highest chart position. Four brilliant records followed with *Master Of Reality, Black Sabbath Volume 4, Sabbath Bloody Sabbath*, and *Sabotage*. *Sabbath Bloody Sabbath* (1973) was undoubtedly the high point artistically, with the band at the pinnacle of their career.

By 1977 personnel difficulties and the rock 'n' roll lifestyle were taking their toll, and Ozzy finally left the band. All in all, Sabbath then went through 11 vocalist line-up changes, including Ronnie James Dio and Ian Gillan, but during the 80s the former magic was never recaptured. The 90s saw Sabbath enter a renaissance, with new interest from bands such as Nirvana and Soundgarden. The band finally reunited in 1997, 20 years after Ozzy had originally left, and a live album *Reunion* (1998) ensued, ensuring the band continued success into the new millennium. A new studio album is even in the offing.

Evolving out of the band Sparrow, Steppenwolf was formed in 1967 with John Kay on vocals, Michael Monarch on guitar, Goldy McJohn on keyboards, Rushton Moreve on bass and Jerry Edmonton on drums. Their self-titled debut in 1968, recorded in just four days included the classic *Born To Be Wild* which included the first ever reference to 'heavy metal'. The song was featured in the opening sequence of the film *Easy Rider*, and as well as cultivating a hardcore biker following, it cemented their reputation as a menacing hard-rock outfit.

Best-selling albums *Steppenwolf The Second, At Your Birthday Party, Monster, Steppenwolf 7*, and *For Ladies Only* followed, producing hits such as *Magic Carpet Ride* and *Rock Me*. There were various personnel changes during this time, including guitarist Monarch being replaced by Larry Byrom and then Kent Henry.

Steppenwolf's popularity continued into the 70s, but the band had burned out by 1972, and completed a successful farewell tour of Europe in 1974. Kay then reformed the band with Jerry Edmonton, Goldy McJohn, George Biondo and new guitarist Bobby Cochran, and recorded three new studio albums, before splitting again in 1976.

In 1980 Kay launched a new line-up billed as John Kay and Steppenwolf, and spent several years grafting on the touring circuit. In 1994, he returned to Germany 25 years after the band's inception for some triumphant Steppenwolf concerts. That same year he released his autobiography *Magic Carpet Ride*.

Today, the band continues to generate new music as well as CD reissues.

Eric 'Slowhand' Clapton, the world's premier blues guitar hero, first received a guitar at the age of 14, and went on to learn the music of the great blues guitarists note for note. His first band was the Roosters, and shortly afterwards Casey Jones and the Engineers. This brief stint ended in 1963 when he was sought by the aspiring R&B band The Yardbirds. After 18 months, musical differences took their toll, but not before they had recorded *For Your Love*.

A short stint with John Mayall's Bluesbreakers earned him the nickname 'God', and then followed numerous sessions including the Powerhouse, comprising Paul Jones, Steve Winwood and Jack Bruce. In 1966, worldwide fame was guaranteed with the formation of Cream (with Jack Bruce and Ginger Baker), one of the most influential rock bands of all time. During this time he also guested on George Harrison's 'While My Guitar Gently Weeps' from The Beatles' *White Album*.

After the break-up of Cream two years later and a brief stint with supergroup Blind Faith in 1969, Clapton went into the most successful phase of his career, not only as a lead guitar player, but also as a singer. The first solo album *Eric Clapton* in 1970 marked this move, and the subsequent *Layla* (recorded later that year with Derek and the Dominos) became a guitar classic.

After a period of drug rehab, Clapton emerged with *461 Ocean Boulevard* in 1974, with notably shorter, more compact songs and no long solos. It included the huge Bob Marley cover 'I Shot The Sheriff'. During 1977 and 1978 he released two more successful studio albums, *Slowhand* and *Backless*, which included the commercial successes 'Lay Down Sally' and 'Cocaine'.

Clapton was well received during the 80s, particularly with the release of *Journeyman* in 1989 which saw a return to some of his finest guitar playing. During the 90s he contributed to many artists' albums, as well as finding time for the hugely successful *Unplugged* in 1992 which included the poignant 'Tears In Heaven'.

Further releases including *Pilgrim* (1998) a soul-based album, have continued his success, but more recently he has been helping other drug addicts at Crossroads, the rehab centre he founded in Antigua.

Eric continues to be hugely successful, and has more than earned the right to be the world's most celebrated white blues guitarist.

PERFORMANCE NOTES

PARANOID – Black Sabbath

The title track from Black Sabbath's 1970 album, *Paranoid*, opens with one of rock's all time classic riffs. This intro riff is based around an E5 chord and the E minor pentatonic scale (E, G, A, B, D, E).

Throughout this song, Tony Iommi explores the idea of paranoia with his two guitar parts, which both mirror and contradict each other. Good examples of this can be found in both the rhythm guitar parts and the guitar solo.

Although Ozzy's vocal line is firmly in the key of E minor, the tonality of the song is less clear if we look at the guitar parts in isolation. The verse starts with both guitars in unison playing E5 and D5 with a palm muted 8th note rhythm. E5 does not contain a 3rd (G♯ or G), so we cannot say whether the guitars are implying an E major or E minor tonality. This is further confused in the following bar (bar 12, for example) where guitar one (left channel) plays an E minor chord and guitar two (right channel) plays the note of G♯ which implies an E major chord. In the middle 8 the guitars both play E major chords, however, the vocal line is still in E minor. This musical guessing game which Iommi plays contributes to the over-all unsettled quality of the song, it appears that Iommi's intention is to make the listener paranoid by never letting them know whether what they are listening to is major or minor!

The guitar solo is played with an effect unit called a ring modulator. The lead guitar is split into two channels and panned left and right. The right channel is the ring modulator effect and the left channel is the dry guitar. The solo uses E minor pentatonic (E, G, A, B, D, E) but the ring modulator makes Iommi's rock/blues licks sound manic by generating a dissonant accompaniment.

To achieve the punchy rhythm guitar sound heard on the record, you should pick using down strokes only. This track was probably recorded with Iommi's Gibson SG (strung with very light strings, such as gauge 8's) through his 100 watt Laney amplifier.

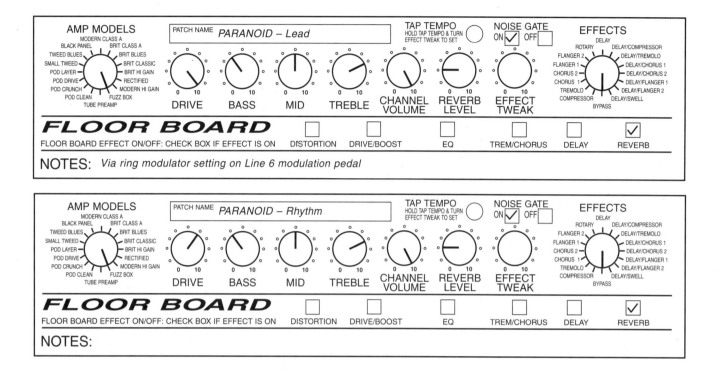

NOTES: *Via ring modulator setting on Line 6 modulation pedal*

LAYLA – Eric Clapton

Eric's biggest anthem, ironically from the Derek And The Dominos period, when Eric was keeping a relatively low profile! This track features many overdubbed layers of guitar, probably played on 'Blackie', the famous vintage Strat which was his main guitar for many years.

The solo figure during the intro and choruses is based around the D minor pentatonic scale; D, F, G, A, C. The verse features a surprise key change to C# minor, so the improvised sounding lead lines over these sections are taken from the corresponding C# blues scale; C#, E, F#, G, G#, B. The rhythm guitar is included on the backing track. After the last chorus, the main lead guitar is joined by an ultra high register slide solo, played by Duane Allman on the original recording. This is also included on the backing right through the piano outro, with our focus being on the arpeggiated chords played by Eric. These are processed with a flange/chorus effect.

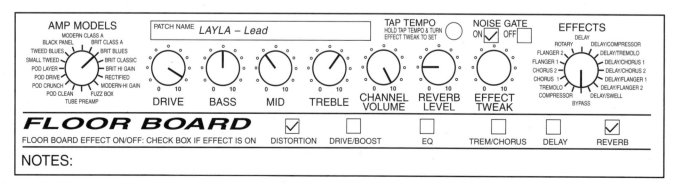

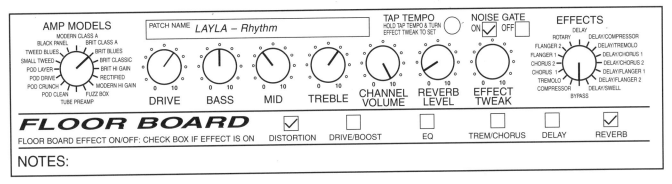

AMP MODELS
MODERN CLASS A · BLACK PANEL · BRIT CLASS A · TWEED BLUES · BRIT BLUES · SMALL TWEED · BRIT CLASSIC · POD LAYER · BRIT HI GAIN · POD DRIVE · RECTIFIED · POD CRUNCH · MODERN HI GAIN · POD CLEAN · FUZZ BOX · TUBE PREAMP

PATCH NAME *LAYLA – Rhythm*

TAP TEMPO — HOLD TAP TEMPO & TURN EFFECT TWEAK TO SET

NOISE GATE — ON ☑ OFF ☐

EFFECTS
DELAY · ROTARY · DELAY/COMPRESSOR · FLANGER 2 · DELAY/TREMOLO · FLANGER 1 · DELAY/CHORUS 1 · CHORUS 2 · DELAY/CHORUS 2 · CHORUS 1 · DELAY/FLANGER 1 · TREMOLO · DELAY/FLANGER 2 · COMPRESSOR · DELAY/SWELL · BYPASS

DRIVE | BASS | MID | TREBLE | CHANNEL VOLUME | REVERB LEVEL | EFFECT TWEAK

FLOOR BOARD

FLOOR BOARD EFFECT ON/OFF: CHECK BOX IF EFFECT IS ON

DISTORTION ☑ | DRIVE/BOOST ☐ | EQ ☐ | TREM/CHORUS ☐ | DELAY ☐ | REVERB ☑

NOTES:

FREE BIRD – Lynyrd Skynyrd

This epic track featured on the band's debut album *Lynyrd Skynyrd* (1973). It was written as a tribute to slide player Duane Allman, and the laidback bottleneck intro is very reminiscent of the guitarist's style.

The intro/verse slide melody is based on the G major scale (G, A, B, C, D, E, F♯) with F naturals used over the F major chords and C♯s used over the D major chords. The feel is very laidback, almost lazy, so aim for slow even slides in between notes. Where a 0 fret indication is given, this generally means the bottleneck is played next to the nut. Also note the 'played slightly flat' indications. These are generally used to flatten the C♯s at the 14th fret (e.g. bar 24) to make them sound bluesier. This means angling the bottleneck slightly so that it can play between the 13th and 14th frets on the B string, and the 14th fret on the G string.

After a short accelerando at the end of the slide section it moves into the famous five minute playout. It features only three chords (G5, B♭5 and C5) and so is almost exclusively based on the G minor pentatonic scale. Guitarist Allen Collins uses a huge amount of bending and pull-offs, based around standard pentatonic ideas, but the speed, accuracy and energetic vibrato is what gives the solo section its excitement. The track features a second guitar part that doubles the main part but breaks off later on.

A lot of fret hand stamina is required for the bending, especially at bar 163-166 where some rapid prebends are needed. These bars are given a 'dizzying' quality by the two guitars being slightly out of sync. Many full tone bends and pull-offs follow in bars 167-190, and the soloing here uses several repeated phrases. At bar 191 the beginning of the solo is used again, this time an octave lower. The next challenge occurs at bar 211, where the two guitars do a fast break over some stabbed accompaniment. As before, Collins uses repeated phrases which again requires a lot of stamina due to the constant playing. This section ends with a very fast, very tricky nontuplet pull-off idea. At bar 235 a simple melody idea is introduced which begins the long crescendo. This idea is expanded with double-stopped chords and bending right up until bar 259 where the crescendo builds with some full tone bending licks. The outro section from bar 275 on, moves back to G minor pentatonic at the 15th fret, and uses ideas taken from previous sections of the solo. The track was probably recorded with Gibson Les Pauls, Flying Vees and Marshall amps.

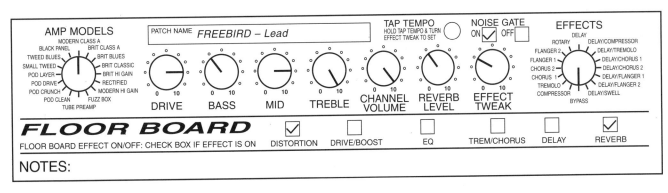

AMP MODELS
MODERN CLASS A · BLACK PANEL · BRIT CLASS A · TWEED BLUES · BRIT BLUES · SMALL TWEED · BRIT CLASSIC · POD LAYER · BRIT HI GAIN · POD DRIVE · RECTIFIED · POD CRUNCH · MODERN HI GAIN · POD CLEAN · FUZZ BOX · TUBE PREAMP

PATCH NAME *FREEBIRD – Lead*

TAP TEMPO — HOLD TAP TEMPO & TURN EFFECT TWEAK TO SET

NOISE GATE — ON ☑ OFF ☐

EFFECTS
DELAY · ROTARY · DELAY/COMPRESSOR · FLANGER 2 · DELAY/TREMOLO · FLANGER 1 · DELAY/CHORUS 1 · CHORUS 2 · DELAY/CHORUS 2 · CHORUS 1 · DELAY/FLANGER 1 · TREMOLO · DELAY/FLANGER 2 · COMPRESSOR · DELAY/SWELL · BYPASS

DRIVE | BASS | MID | TREBLE | CHANNEL VOLUME | REVERB LEVEL | EFFECT TWEAK

FLOOR BOARD

FLOOR BOARD EFFECT ON/OFF: CHECK BOX IF EFFECT IS ON

DISTORTION ☑ | DRIVE/BOOST ☐ | EQ ☐ | TREM/CHORUS ☐ | DELAY ☐ | REVERB ☑

NOTES:

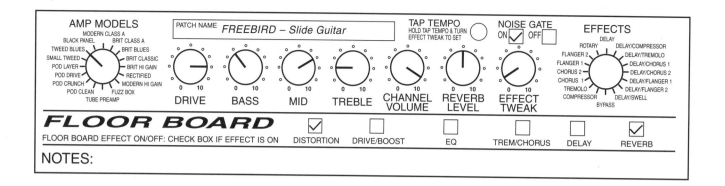

AMP MODELS

MODERN CLASS A
BLACK PANEL   BRIT CLASS A
TWEED BLUES   BRIT BLUES
SMALL TWEED   BRIT CLASSIC
POD LAYER   BRIT HI GAIN
POD DRIVE   RECTIFIED
POD CRUNCH   MODERN HI GAIN
POD CLEAN   FUZZ BOX
   TUBE PREAMP

PATCH NAME *FREEBIRD – Slide Guitar*

TAP TEMPO
HOLD TAP TEMPO & TURN
EFFECT TWEAK TO SET

NOISE GATE
ON ☑ OFF ☐

EFFECTS
                              DELAY
                    ROTARY   DELAY/COMPRESSOR
          FLANGER 2   DELAY/TREMOLO
          FLANGER 1   DELAY/CHORUS 1
          CHORUS 2   DELAY/CHORUS 2
          CHORUS 1   DELAY/FLANGER 1
          TREMOLO   DELAY/FLANGER 2
       COMPRESSOR   DELAY/SWELL
                    BYPASS

DRIVE   BASS   MID   TREBLE   CHANNEL VOLUME   REVERB LEVEL   EFFECT TWEAK

FLOOR BOARD

FLOOR BOARD EFFECT ON/OFF: CHECK BOX IF EFFECT IS ON

DISTORTION ☑   DRIVE/BOOST ☐   EQ ☐   TREM/CHORUS ☐   DELAY ☐   REVERB ☑

NOTES:

SWEET HOME ALABAMA – Lynyrd Skynyrd

Lynyrd Skynyrd recorded their second album *Second Helping* (1974) with three guitarists – Gary Rossington, Allen Collins and Ed King. With its instantly identifiable riff and chorus, *Sweet Home Alabama* remains their biggest hit after *Free Bird*. Most of the rhythm parts were handled by King and Rossington, with Collins taking lead duty for the two solos.

The intro/verse riff is based on a simple D5, Cadd9, G chord progression, with tight picking, staccato notes and country hammer-ons. A second riff comes in at bar 17 using chromatic passing notes to vary the sound of the chord progression. When the chorus comes in, the rhythm part begins to use bluesy double-stopped D/C/G5 and 6 chords. This is treated with staccato effects and string mutes as well as more hammer-on ideas.

The first solo at bar 37 uses a lot of characteristic Collins ideas. It's based on the G major pentatonic scale (G, A, B, D, E, G) with some chromatic B♭ and D♯ passing notes, and the odd F♯ and C borrowed from the full G major scale. It's mostly semiquaver based with quite a bit of sliding around to keep the momentum going. At the end of the solo, Collins executes a slight tremolo arm dip, an idea which he later uses in solo 2 and in a short lick before verse 4.

Solo 2 - again based on G major pentatonic - begins with some short semitone bends and a small pentatonic lick higher up the neck. The 5th bar sees Collins blister through a rapid hemiola pull-off pattern which includes the C from the major scale. Bar 9 again uses some characteristic sliding ideas, and the following two bars use some aggressive vibrato on the high G. Collins keeps the semiquaver momentum throughout the final bars with predominantly two note per string sliding and hammer-on pentatonic ideas. Three bars before verse 4 sees a brief build up to a lovely natural harmonic idea that employs the whammy bar to alter the pitch of the final harmonic. For this track, Rossington used a Gibson Les Paul, King used a Fender Stratocaster and Collins used a Gibson Firebird, probably through Marshall amps.

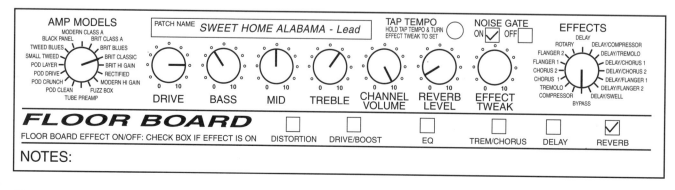

AMP MODELS

MODERN CLASS A
BLACK PANEL   BRIT CLASS A
TWEED BLUES   BRIT BLUES
SMALL TWEED   BRIT CLASSIC
POD LAYER   BRIT HI GAIN
POD DRIVE   RECTIFIED
POD CRUNCH   MODERN HI GAIN
POD CLEAN   FUZZ BOX
   TUBE PREAMP

PATCH NAME *SWEET HOME ALABAMA - Lead*

TAP TEMPO
HOLD TAP TEMPO & TURN
EFFECT TWEAK TO SET

NOISE GATE
ON ☑ OFF ☐

EFFECTS
                              DELAY
                    ROTARY   DELAY/COMPRESSOR
          FLANGER 2   DELAY/TREMOLO
          FLANGER 1   DELAY/CHORUS 1
          CHORUS 2   DELAY/CHORUS 2
          CHORUS 1   DELAY/FLANGER 1
          TREMOLO   DELAY/FLANGER 2
       COMPRESSOR   DELAY/SWELL
                    BYPASS

DRIVE   BASS   MID   TREBLE   CHANNEL VOLUME   REVERB LEVEL   EFFECT TWEAK

FLOOR BOARD

FLOOR BOARD EFFECT ON/OFF: CHECK BOX IF EFFECT IS ON

DISTORTION ☐   DRIVE/BOOST ☐   EQ ☐   TREM/CHORUS ☐   DELAY ☐   REVERB ☑

NOTES:

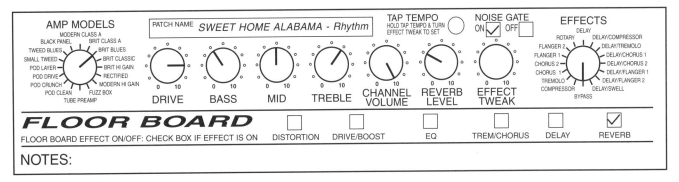

NOTES:

ROCKY MOUNTAIN WAY – Joe Walsh

This landmark track appeared on *The Smoker You Drink, The Player You Get* (1973). Slide guitar - a Walsh speciality - is heard prominently throughout the song, and owes a lot to the influence of slide mentor Duane Allman. Allman personally showed Joe the open E tuning (E, B, E, G♯, B, E) used here, which allows greater scope for slide playing - which can only effectively cover one fret at a time. Because of the different tunings of the main guitar parts, two separate backing tracks are provided.

The track opens with simple 5th to 6th blues/rock shuffle comping, as well as some throbbing low E palm-muting and big E major chords. When the riff moves down to D5 (bars 8-9), the slide guitar enters with some E minor pentatonic improvisation (E, G, A, B, D, E) that outlines the underlining rhythm and D5 chord. As the first short solo finishes at bar 16 the rhythm guitar plays a powerful blues based A to E riff with a laid back bent G in between.

The chorus at bar 25 kicks off with simple A5 to A6 riffing in the rhythm guitars, embellished by a full major triad played by the slide guitar. At the end of the chorus, another short slide section uses similar E minor pentatonic ideas to the first.
The first solo at bar 73 begins to use more of the neck, with some long slides, liberal use of vibrato and a nifty B and D 3rds riff that crops up in the second solo. Once again, the E minor pentatonic is used as well as the outlining 'D5' lick used previously.

Walsh introduces a talk box in the interlude that follows using characteristic E minor pentatonic blues/rock ideas. A second part appears at bar 95 harmonising the main part an octave lower before ushering in the climactic second slide solo.

The solo begins at the end of bar 104 with a passing C-C♯ slide that hints at A major pentatonic (A, B, C♯, E, F♯, A). When the rhythm guitar part goes back to the original D5 to E5/E6 riff, the slide plays once again with E minor pentatonic, this time embellishing a lot of the ideas used earlier. The solo ends with a return to the bluesy A to E5 idea used in bars 16-17. The track was recorded with a Telecaster and a 1954 Stratocaster. One was fitted with Fender Rock 'n' Roll 150s light gauge, and one with heavy gauge and the guitar's action set very high for the slide solos. The amp was probably a customised Fender Twin.

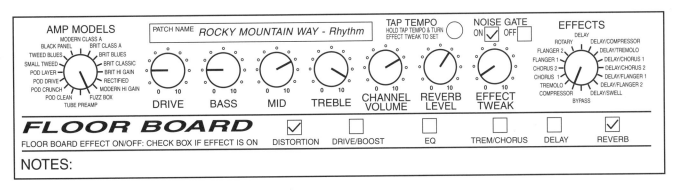

NOTES:

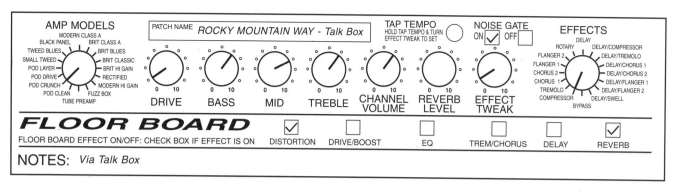

FLOOR BOARD

PATCH NAME *ROCKY MOUNTAIN WAY - Talk Box*

FLOOR BOARD EFFECT ON/OFF: CHECK BOX IF EFFECT IS ON

NOTES: *Via Talk Box*

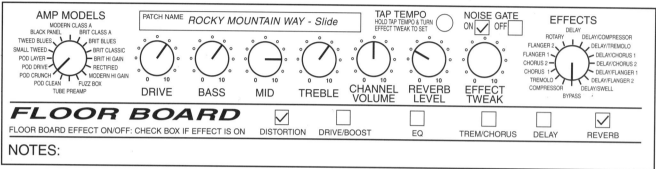

FLOOR BOARD

PATCH NAME *ROCKY MOUNTAIN WAY - Slide*

FLOOR BOARD EFFECT ON/OFF: CHECK BOX IF EFFECT IS ON

NOTES:

MORE THAN A FEELING – Boston

Arguably Boston's most famous track, 'More Than A Feeling' featured on the band's 16 million selling debut album, making it the biggest selling debut in history. The track kicks off with doubled acoustic 12-string guitars playing arpeggiated D, Dsus4, Cadd9, G/B and G chord shapes. The latter half of the intro introduces a clean, compressed natural harmonic melody - the first of many overdubbed guitar parts.

At bar 18, we hear the first example of the classic Boston guitar sound, with a simple, yet effective pre-chorus melody that is doubled in unison and an octave higher, using G Ionian; (G, A, B, C, D, E, F♯, G). Guitarist, producer and creative tour de force, Tom Scholz originally founded a design company in 1980 that developed the renowned Rockman line of products. This helped to recreate the unique trademark sound that was originally created with a wah pedal set at the middle position for a narrow band-pass filter.

The chorus uses a combination of G5, D5 and C5 powerchords, as well as the slightly fuller sounding C major and E minor chords. Clever use of fret-hand string mutes adds plenty of rhythmic interest.

The slightly unusual E♭ minor chord at the end of the chorus heralds the beginning of the bridge. This uses a doubled, clean electric guitar, and utilises simple open position Em7, Asus4, A, Asus2, G and D/F♯ chords before returning to the verse again.

The 2nd time ending of the bridge uses some brief palm-muted chords, before turning on the distortion in preparation for the solo. The solo itself, which is occasionally harmonised in diatonic 3rds by another guitar part, uses the D Ionian scale; (D, E, F♯, G, A, B, C♯). It makes much rhythmic reference to a triplet semiquaver legato idea, that crops up throughout the solo. This section is followed by a short interlude based on the original 12 string part.

This leads into the final verse, which is extended by doubling the acoustic guitar part with the main electric guitars, broken up by some short solo bending ideas.

The outro chorus is essentially the same, although the rhythms are cleverly varied on each cycle. The track was recorded with a Gibson 1968 Goldtop, Jim Dunlop Cry Baby, Yamaha APX9-12 string acoustic, and a Vox Tonebender amp.

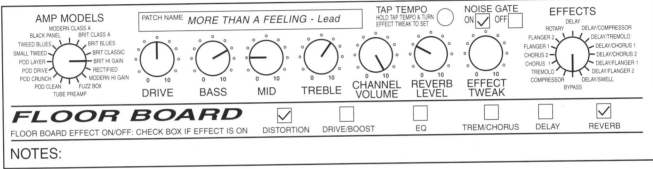

BORN TO BE WILD – Steppenwolf

This track, which appears on the 1968 album *Steppenwolf* and, more famously, on the sound track to the film *Easy Rider*, is where the term 'heavy metal' was first coined (bar 27).

The opening riff and verse, which is based around an E major barre chord, is performed with a tight rhythmic feel. This is achieved by keeping the strumming hand constantly moving up and down in 8th notes whilst applying and releasing pressure with the fretting hand to sound and mute the chords.

In the chorus the guitar swaps seamlessly between chords and E minor pentatonic (E, G, A, B, D, E) fills. The smooth transition is made easier by the fact that each of these licks is preceded by a low E note, thus giving you time to change the position of your fretting hand whilst picking the open string.

The guitar parts were played by Michael Monarch who probably used a Rickenbacker guitar through a Marshall amplifier.

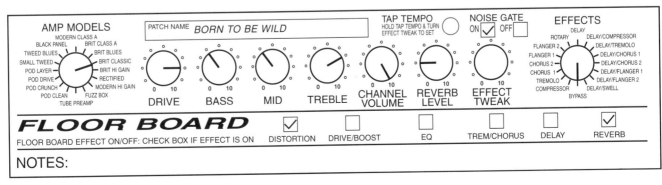

WON'T GET FOOLED AGAIN – The Who

The track appears on The Who's eighth album, *Who's Next* (1971), falling in between *Tommy* (1969) and *Quadrophenia* (1973). It reflects guitarist Pete Townshend's interest in synthesisers, which resulted in an organ plugged into the filter section of an EMS synthesiser for the chordal stuttering.

The intro, verse and chorus sections mainly use simple open position major and powerchord shapes, with a few 1/4 note bends on the low G's, and use of staccato. The end of the chorus sees Townshend's first foray up the fretboard (bars 48-52) with the use of sixth intervals. At bar 61 we are first introduced to a classic Townshend riff that recurs at bar 108, 195 and 278.

The end of the second chorus sees a slight variation, with more lead ideas based loosely around the Em pentatonic scale (E, G, A, B, D, E). The break at bar 100 kicks off with some simple A5 powerchords and leads into the main riff again which has a familiar *Alright Now* (Free) vibe to it. Pete mixes up a few pentatonic lead ideas with the riff before launching into the bridge.

The bridge begins to modulate into B major, with some nice country bending at bar 121 in between. At bar 124 we are now firmly in B major, where Pete plays a simple B, A, E chord progression made more difficult by the syncopation and fret hand string mutes.

The main solo at bar 132 is based in B minor pentatonic (B, D, E, F#, A) with some passing G# and D# notes thrown in. The main guitar and overdubbed part trade off each other using similar rhythmic ideas, 1/4 1/2 and full note bends and hammer-ons.

After another verse and chorus, a second main riff break heralds the second solo which starts at bar 204 with some fast bluesy pull-offs. Pete mainly uses Am pentatonic (A, C, D, E, G, A) in a solo with plenty of bending, slides and pull-offs. After the organ break, Townshend goes back to the A5, G, D idea heard earlier, and then does a variation riff at bar 270, before finishing with the main riff and some stabbed A5 chords.

The track was recorded with a Gretsch Chet Atkins semi through a HiWatt with Marshall 4X12 cabs.

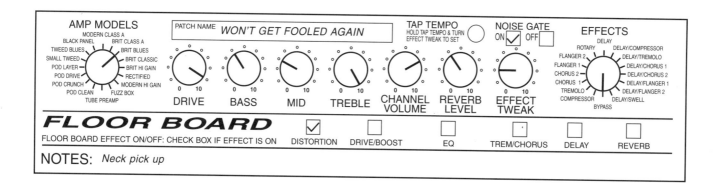

Notation & Tablature Explained

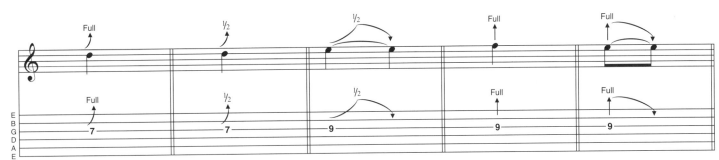

BEND: Strike the note and bend up a whole step (two frets).

BEND: Strike the note and bend up a half step (one fret).

BEND AND RELEASE: Strike the note, bend up a half step, then release the bend.

PRE-BEND: Bend the note up, then strike it.

PRE-BEND AND RELEASE: Bend up, strike the note, then release it.

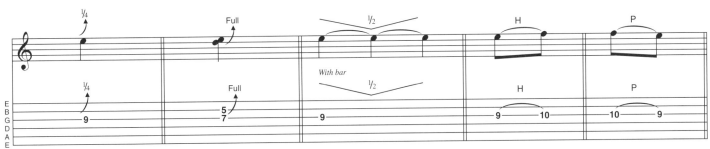

QUARTER-TONE BEND: Bend the note slightly sharp.

UNISON BEND: Strike both notes, then bend the lower note up to the pitch of the higher one.

TREMOLO BAR BENDS: Strike the note, and push the bar down and up by the amounts indicated.

HAMMER-ON: Strike the first note, then sound the second by fretting it without picking.

PULL-OFF: Strike the higher note, then pull the finger off while keeping the lower one fretted.

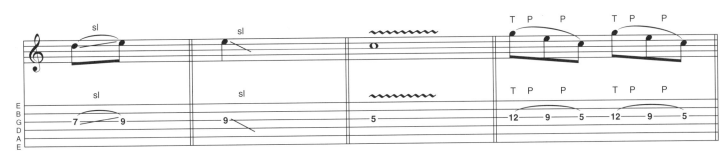

SLIDE: Slide the finger from the first note to the second. Only the first note is struck.

SLIDE: Slide to the fret from a few frets below or above.

VIBRATO: The string is vibrated by rapidly bending and releasing a note with the fretboard hand or tremolo bar.

TAPPING: Hammer on to the note marked with a T using the picking hand, then pull off to the next note, following the hammer-ons or pull-offs in the normal way.

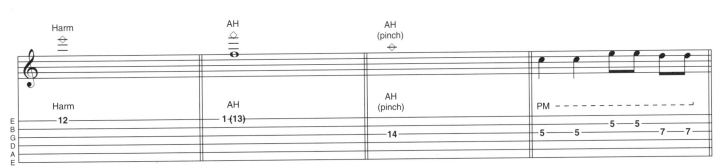

NATURAL HARMONIC: Lightly touch the string directly over the fret shown, then strike the note to create a "chiming" effect.

ARTIFICIAL HARMONIC: Fret the note, then use the picking hand finger to touch the string at the position shown in brackets and pluck with another finger.

ARTIFICIAL HARMONIC: The harmonic is produced by using the edge of the picking hand thumb to "pinch" the string whilst picking firmly with the plectrum.

PALM MUTES: Rest the palm of the picking hand on the strings near the bridge to produce a muted effect. Palm mutes can apply to a single note or a number of notes (shown with a dashed line).

Paranoid

BLACK SABBATH

Words & Music by
Terence Butler, John Osbourne,
Frank Iommi & William Ward

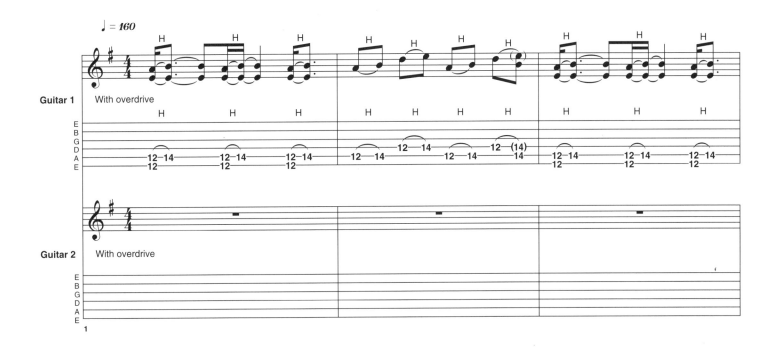

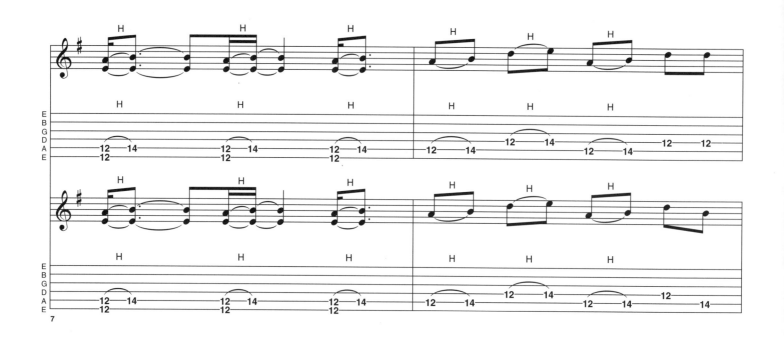

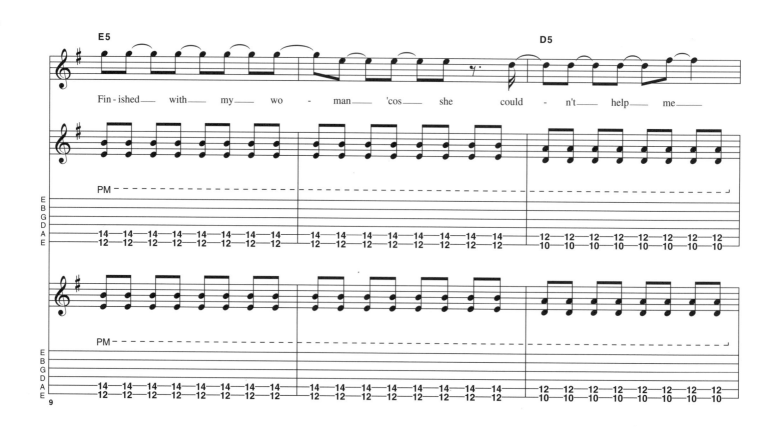

Fin - ished___ with___ my___ wo - man___ 'cos___ she could - n't___ help___ me___

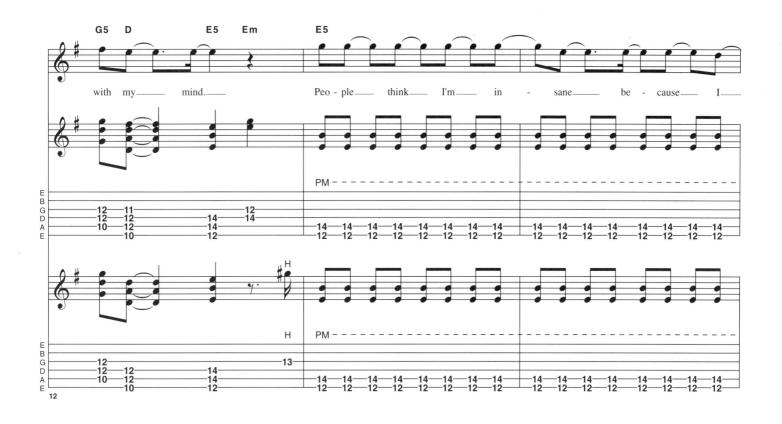

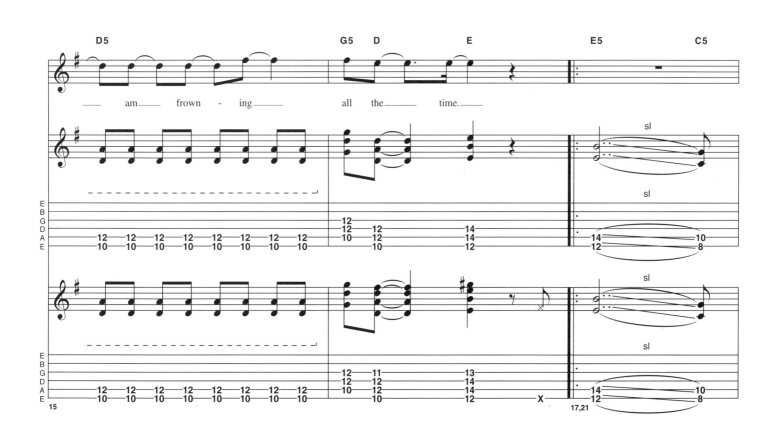

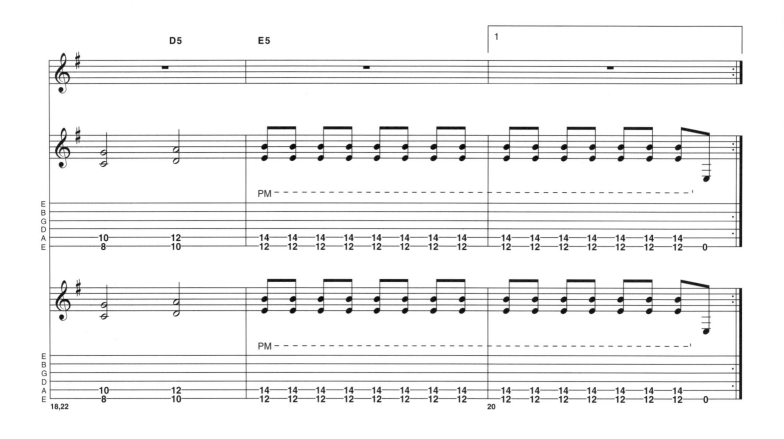

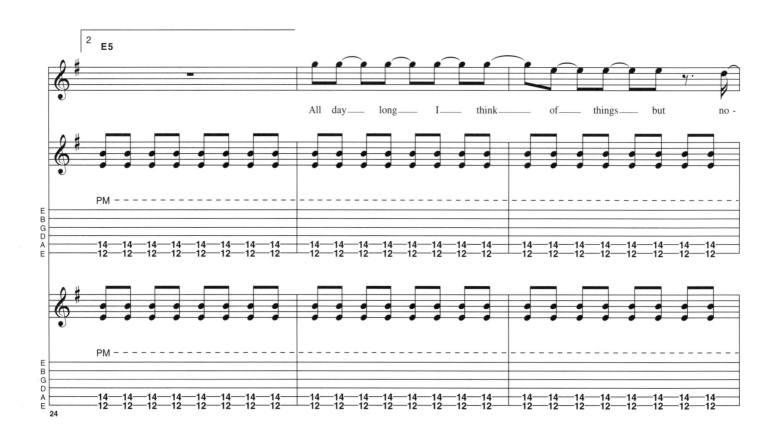

All day—— long—— I—— think—— of—— things—— but—— no-

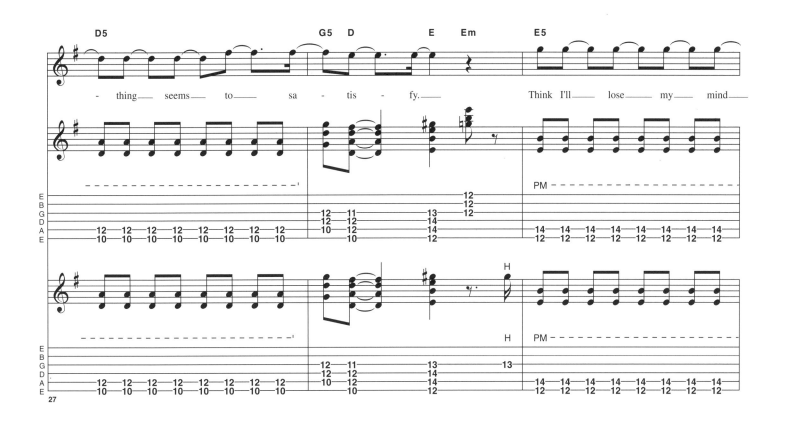

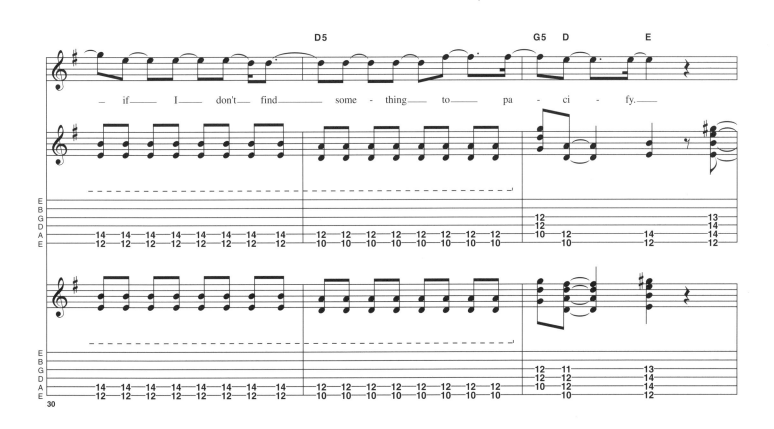

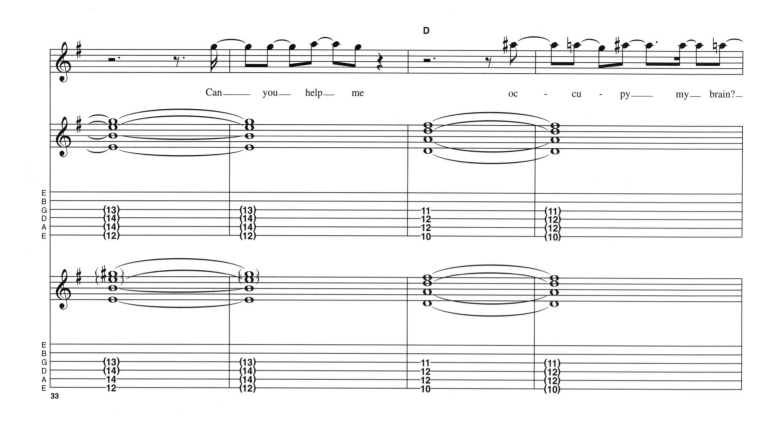

Can——— you—— help—— me   oc - cu - py——— my—— brain?—

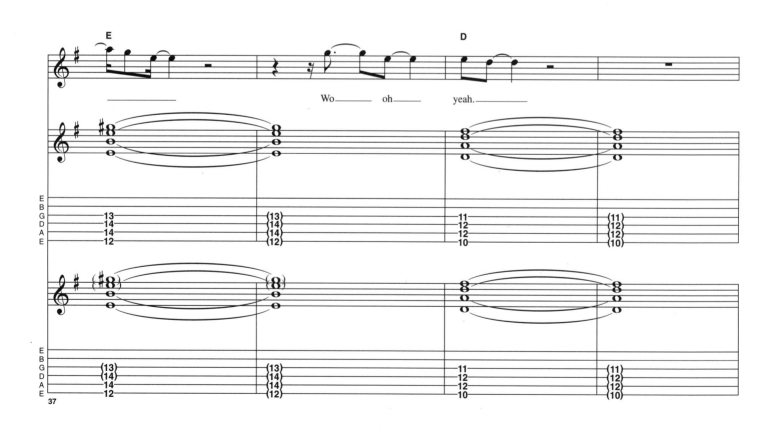

Wo——— oh——— yeah.———

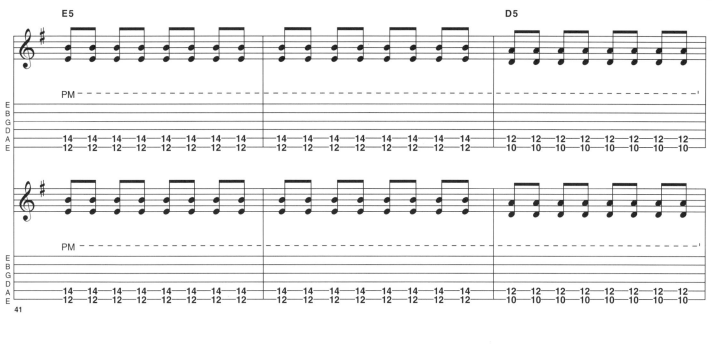

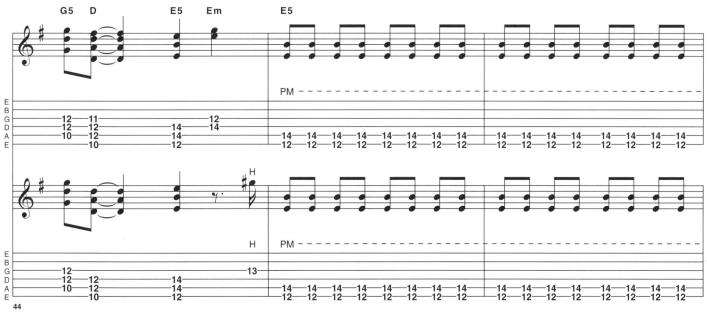

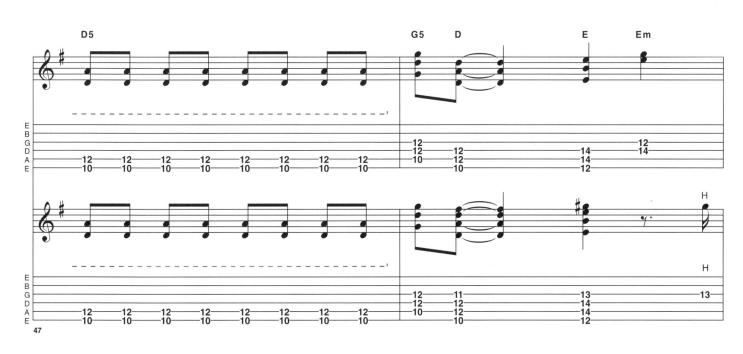

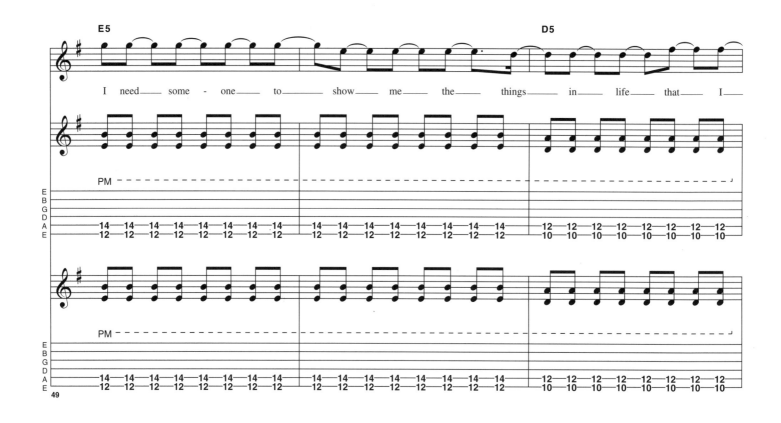

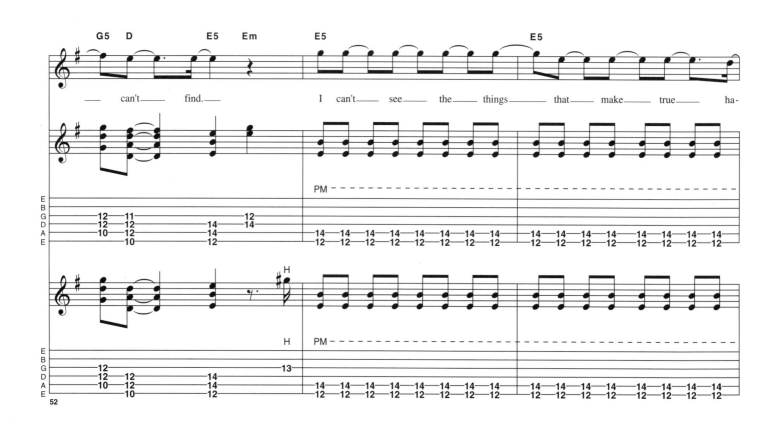

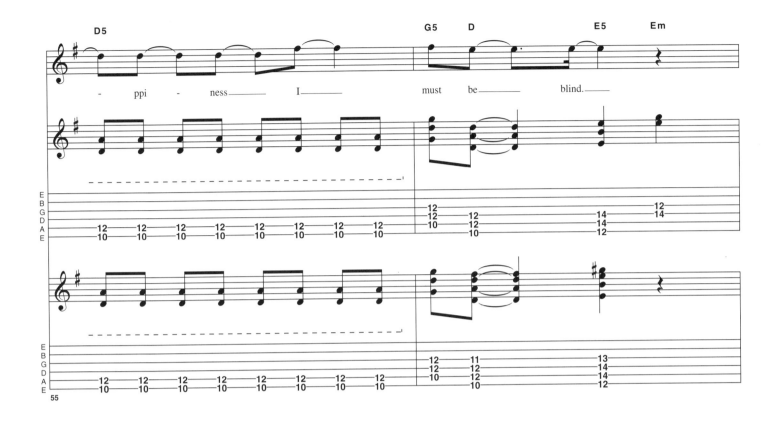

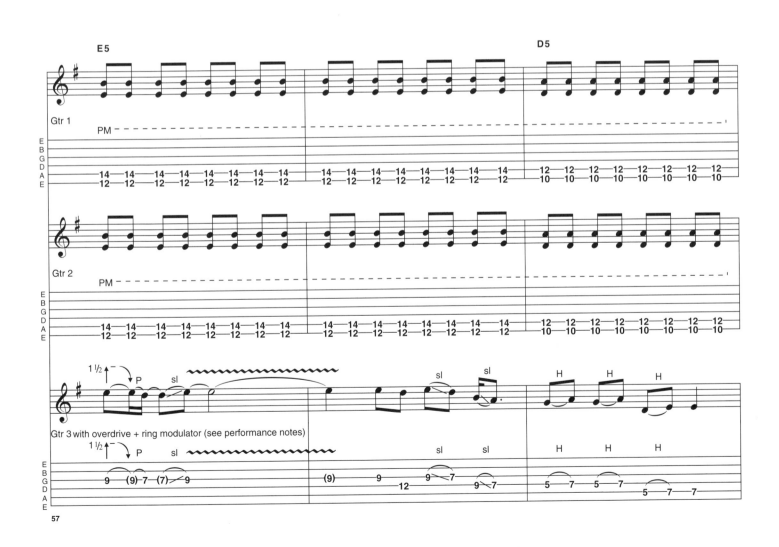

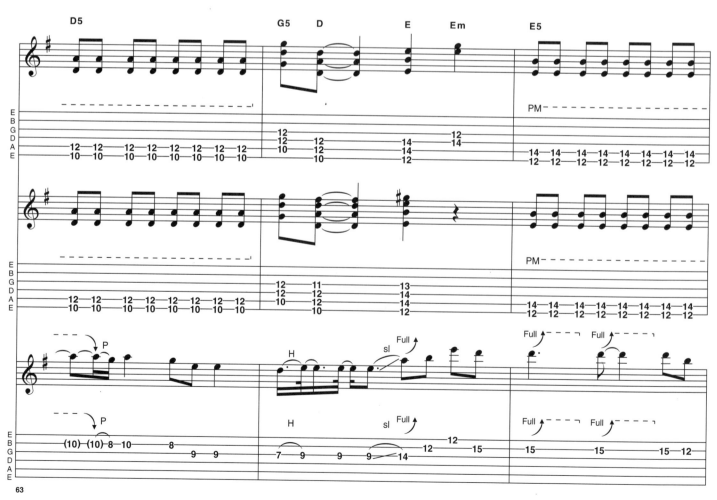

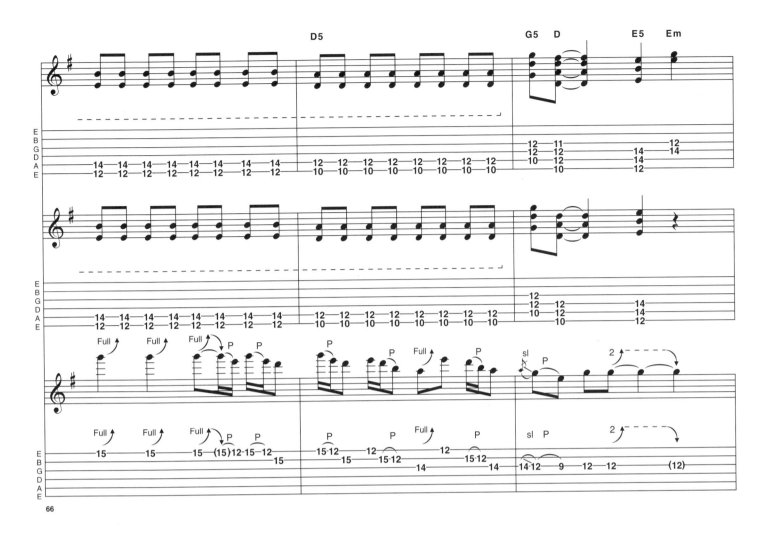

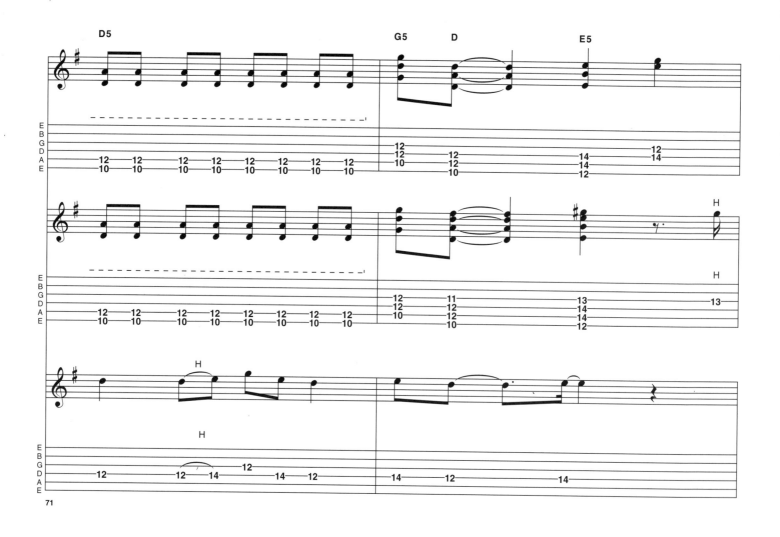

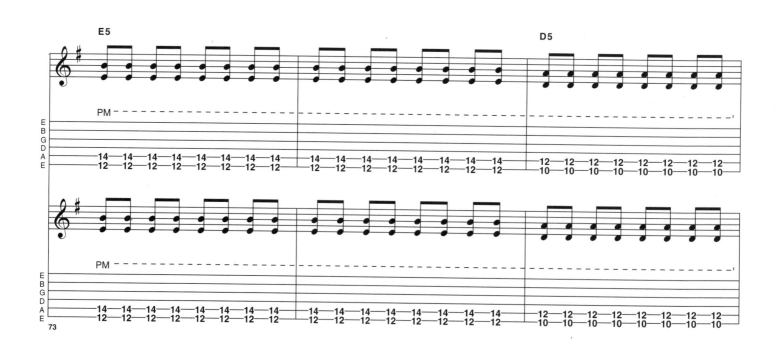

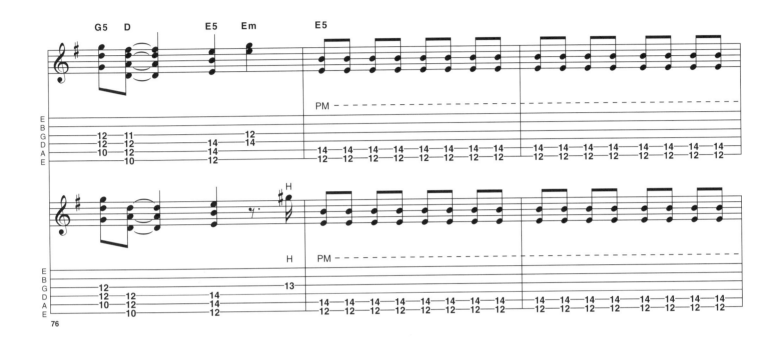

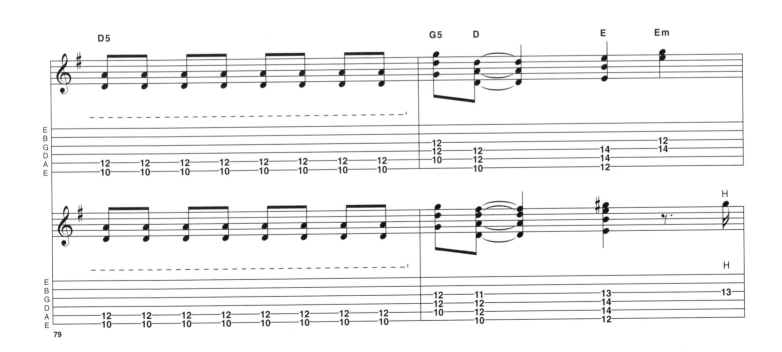

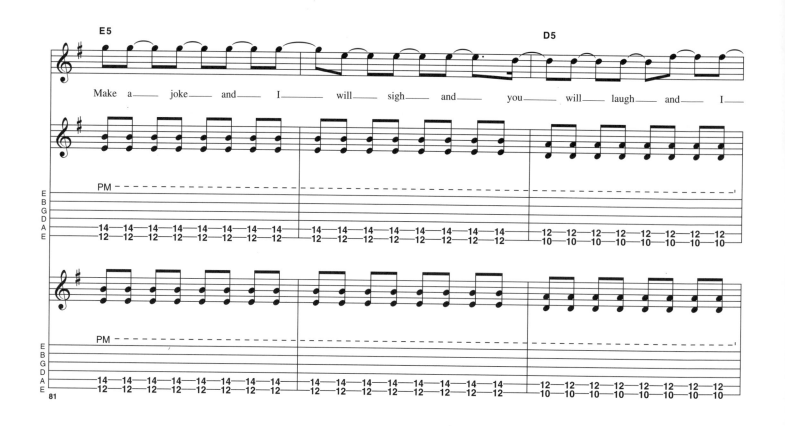

Make a —— joke and —— I —— will —— sigh —— and —— you —— will laugh —— and —— I ——

—— will —— cry. —— Ha - ppi - ness —— I —— can —— not feel —— like —— love

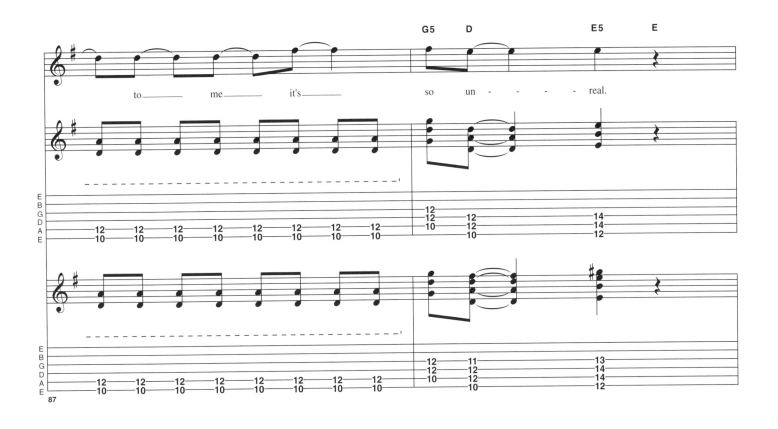

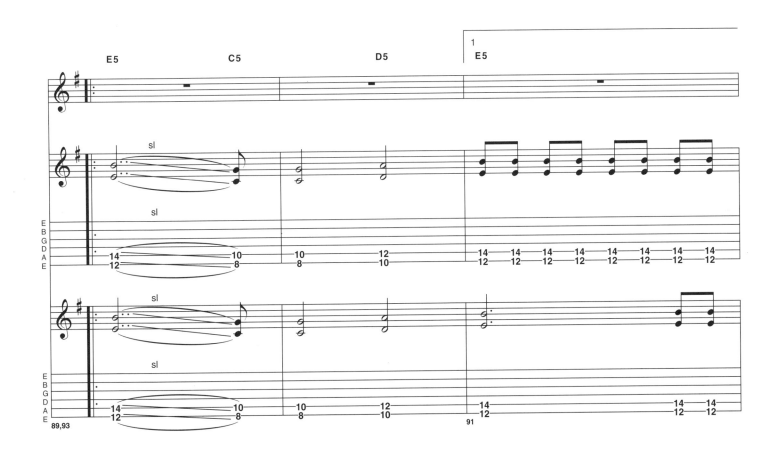

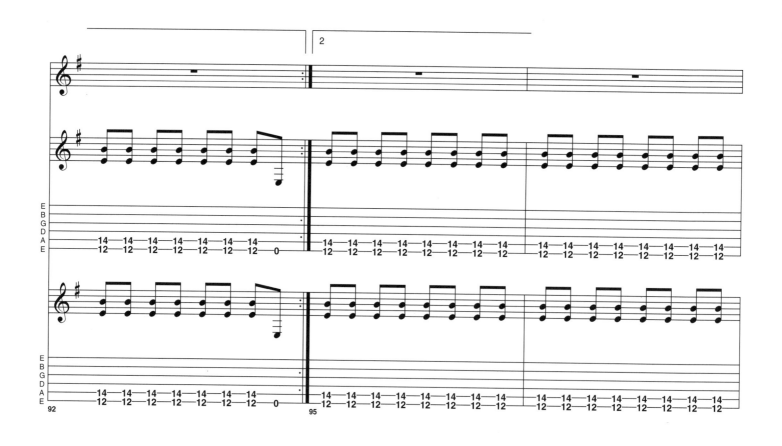

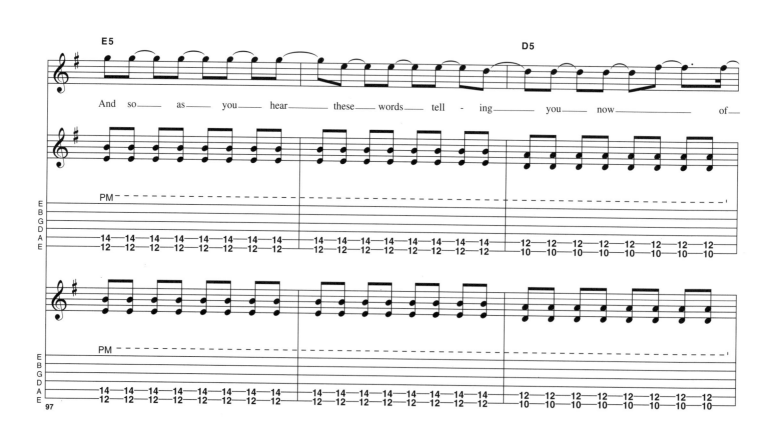

And so— as— you— hear— these— words— tell - ing— you— now— of—

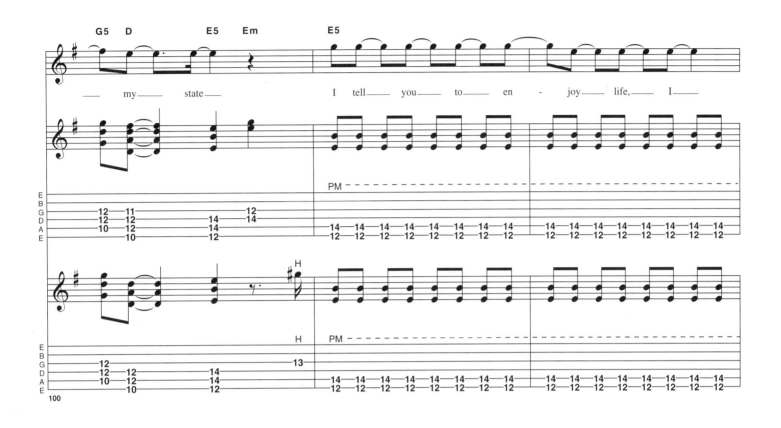

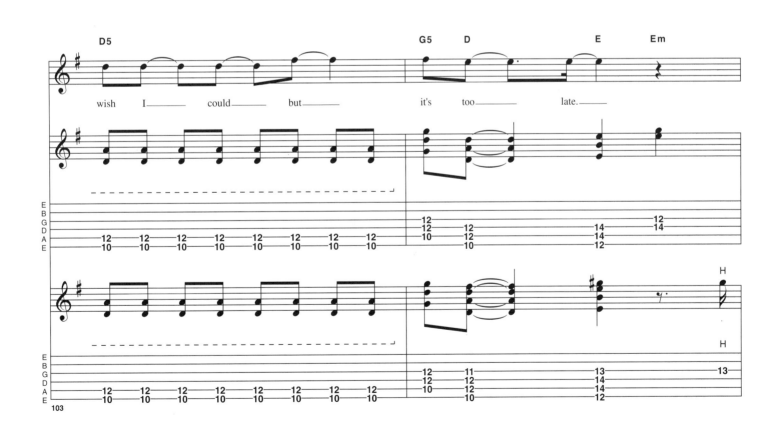

34

Layla

ERIC CLAPTON

Words & Music by
Eric Clapton & Jim Gordon

41

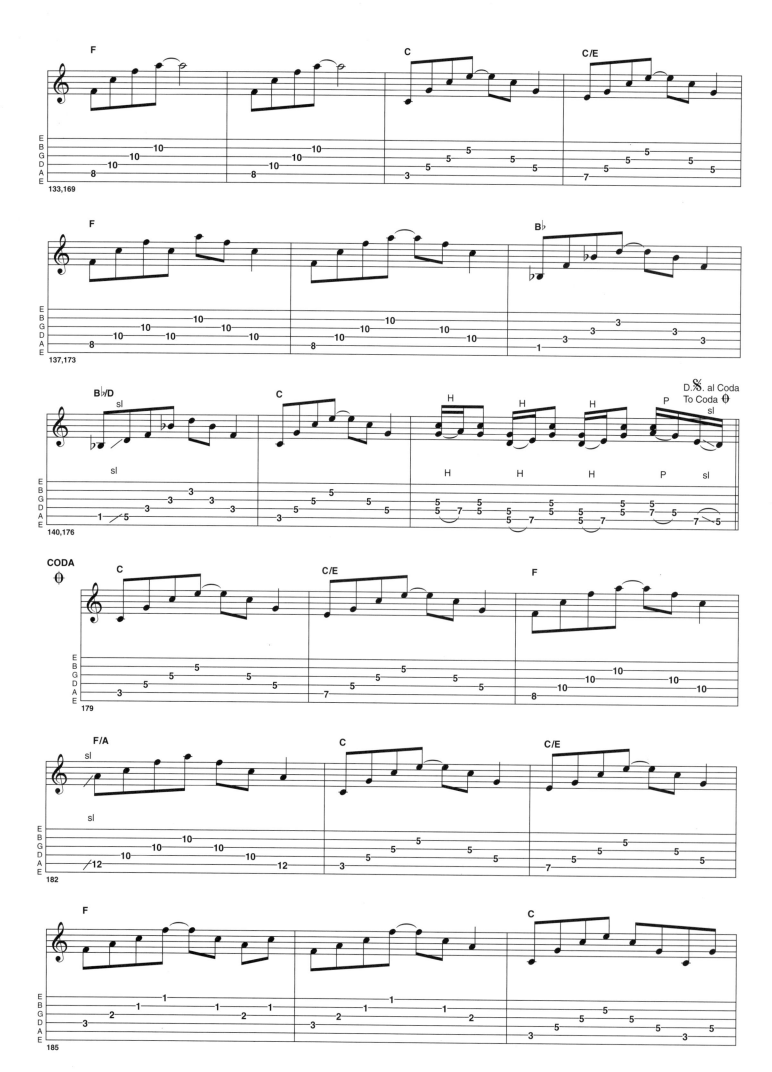

43

Free Bird

LYNYRD SKYNYRD

Words & Music by
Allen Collins & Ronnie Van Zant

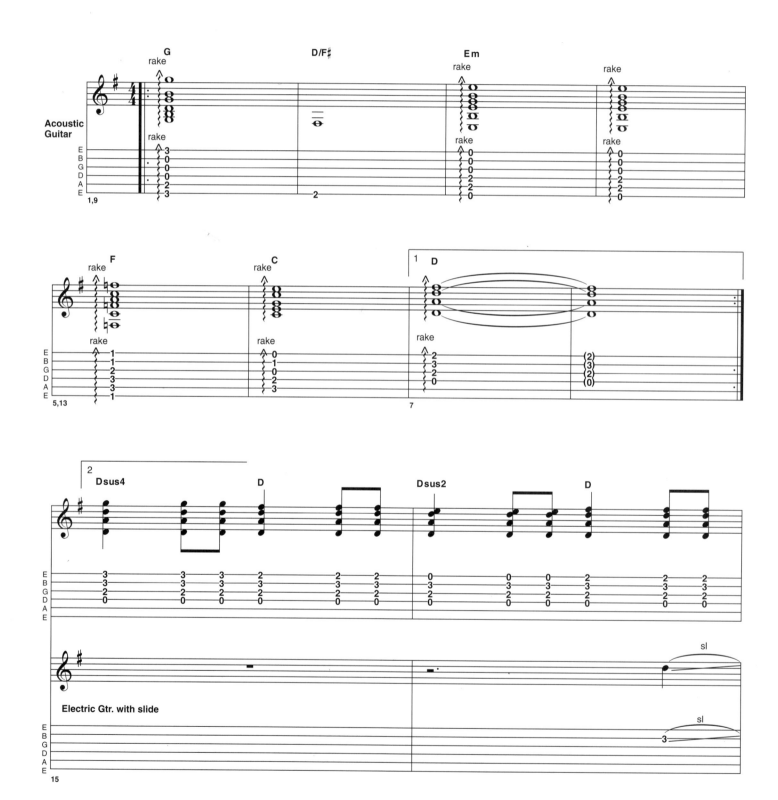

Electric Gtr. with slide

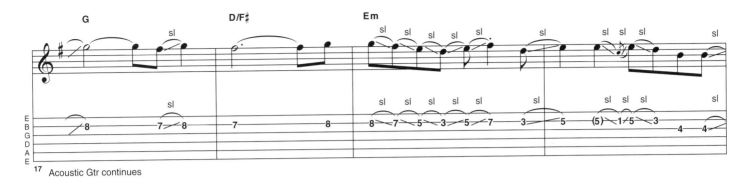

17 Acoustic Gtr continues

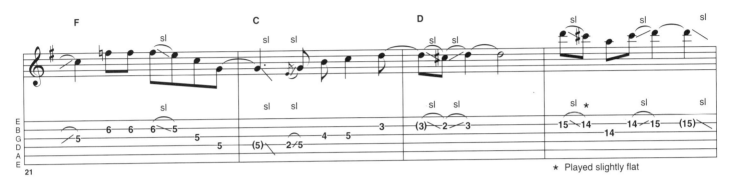

21

★ Played slightly flat

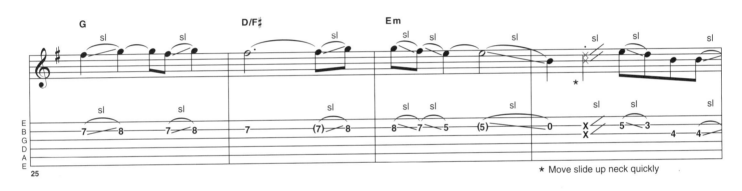

25

★ Move slide up neck quickly

29

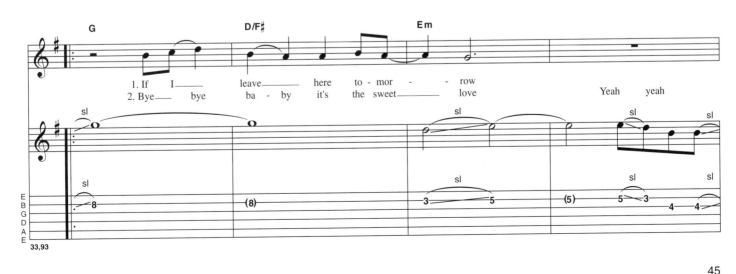

1. If I ___ leave ___ here to - mor - - row
2. Bye ___ bye ba - by it's the sweet ___ love   Yeah   yeah

33,93

would you_____ still re - mem - ber me?_____
Through this_____ feeling I can't_____ change._____

* Hold for semibreve
1st time.

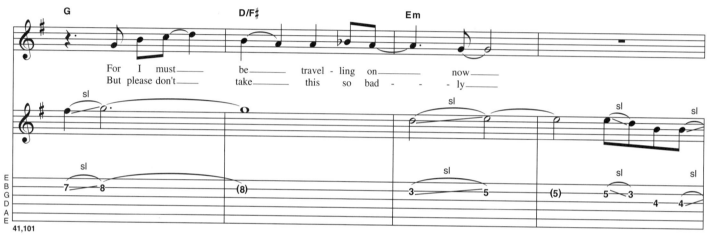

For I must_____ be_____ travel - ling on_____ now_____
But please don't_____ take_____ this so bad - - ly_____

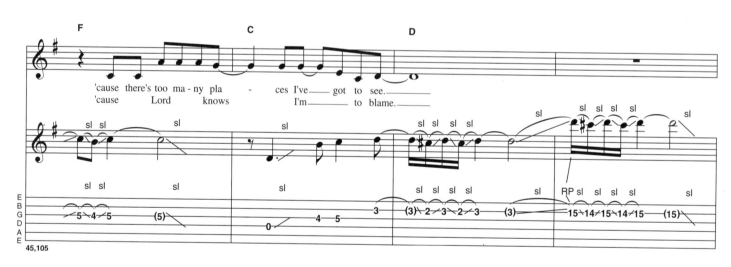

'cause there's too ma - ny pla - - ces I've_____ got to see._____
'cause Lord knows I'm_____ to blame._____

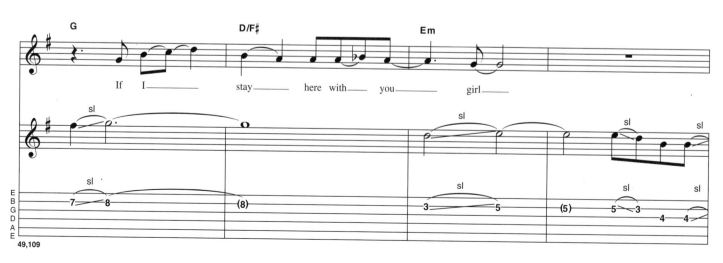

If I_____ stay_____ here with_____ you_____ girl_____

And this bird_____ you can - not change_____

Lord knows I can't_____ change._____

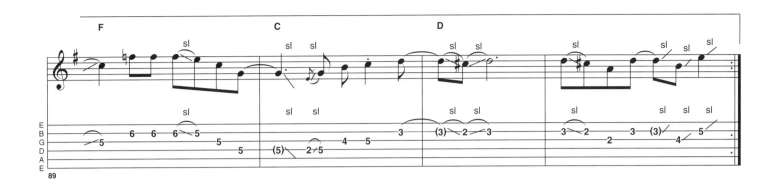

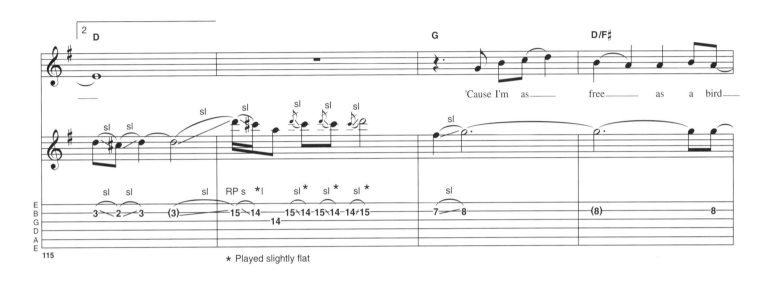

★ Played slightly flat

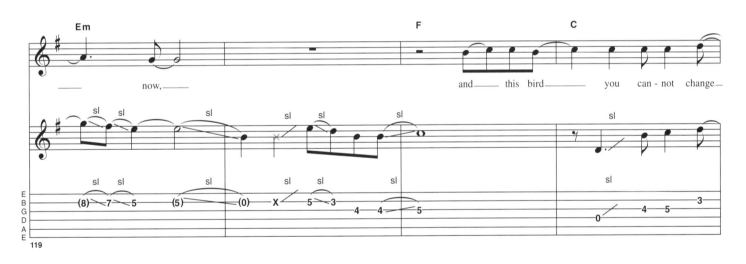

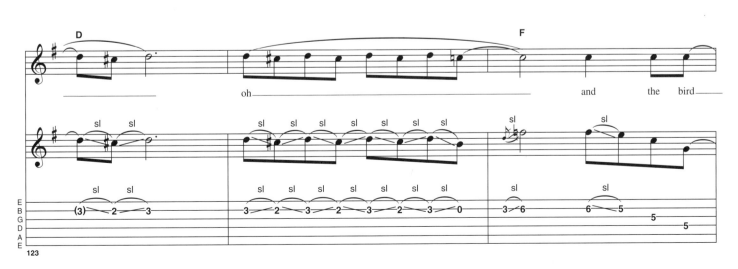

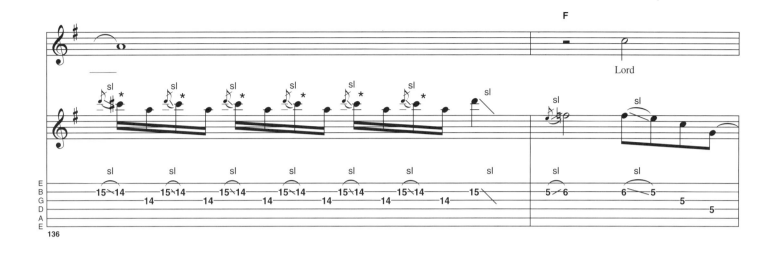

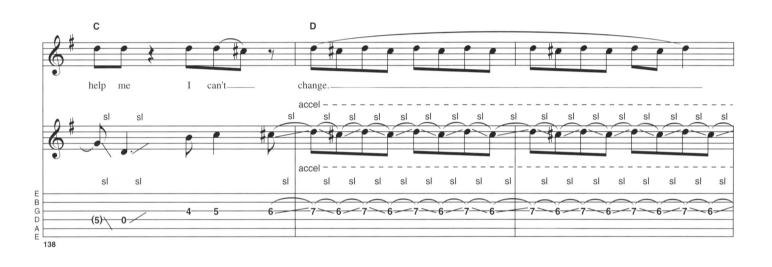

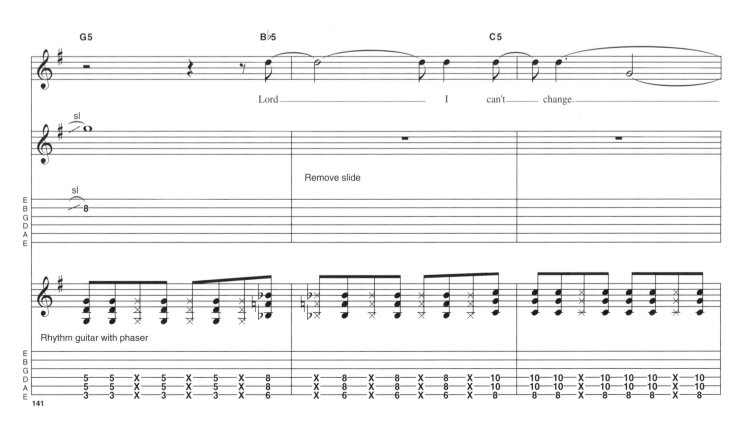

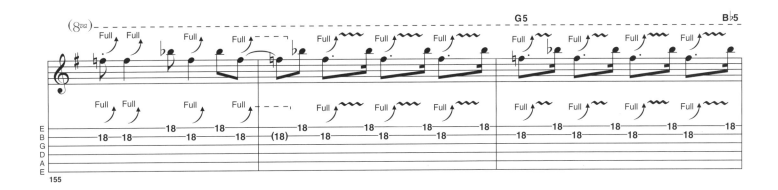

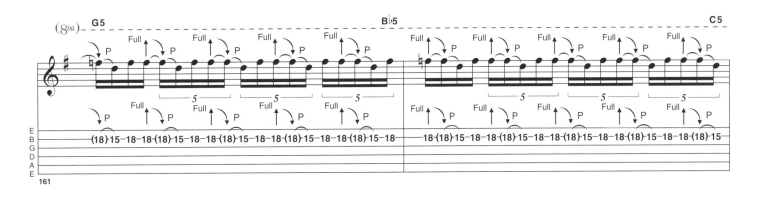

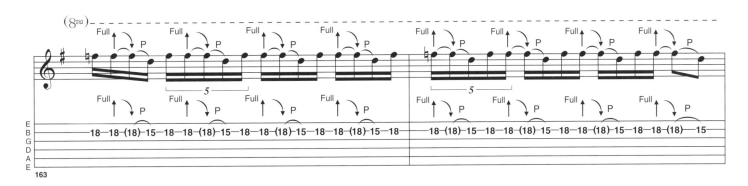

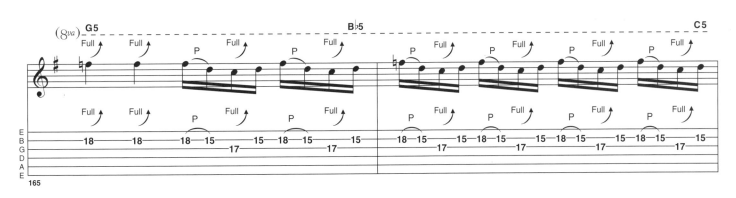

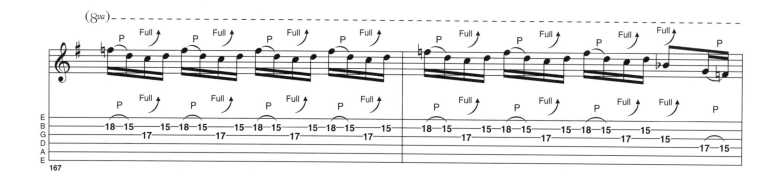

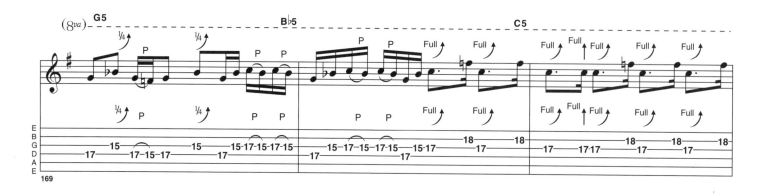

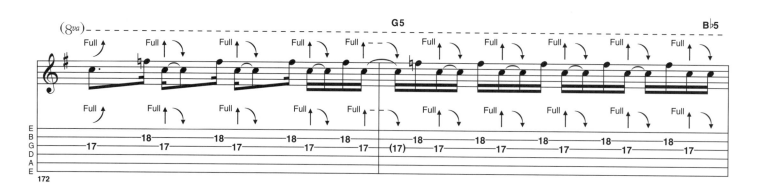

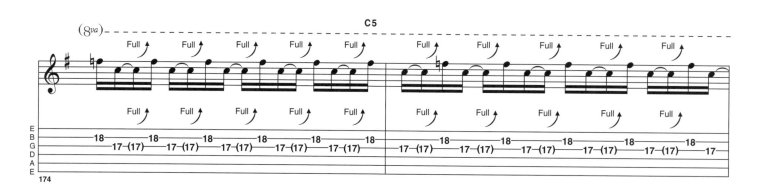

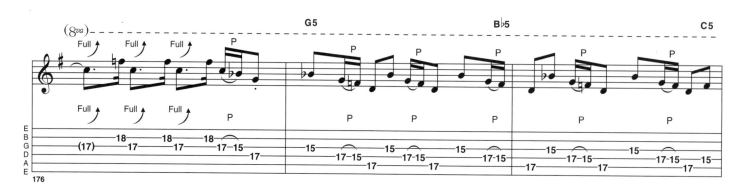

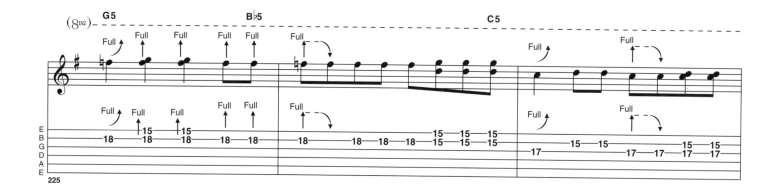

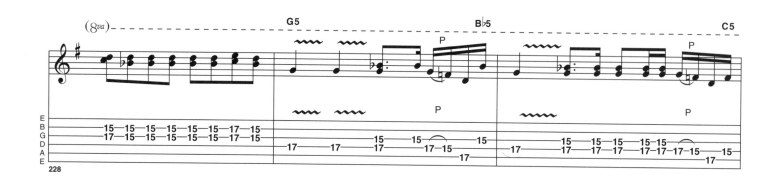

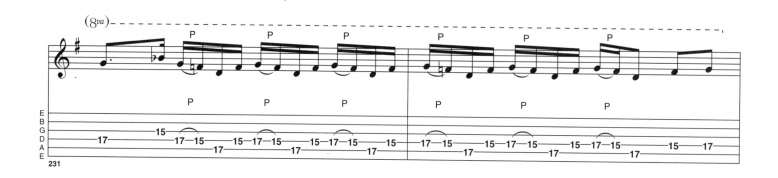

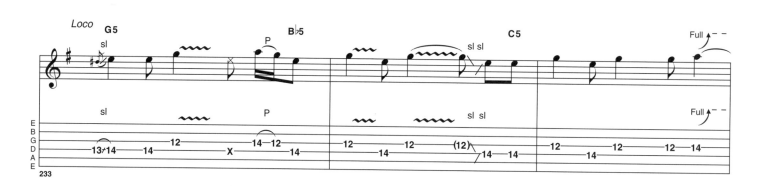

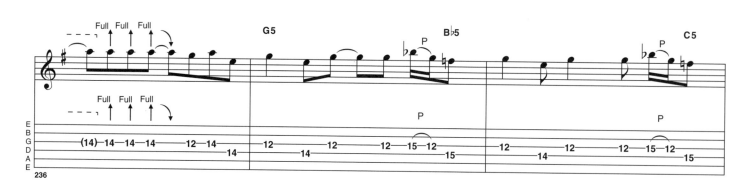

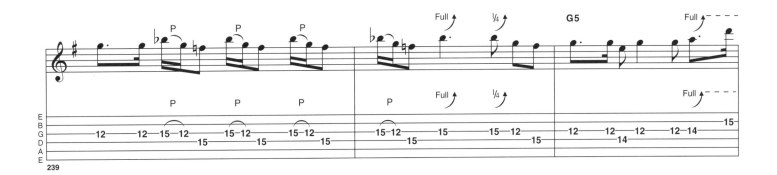

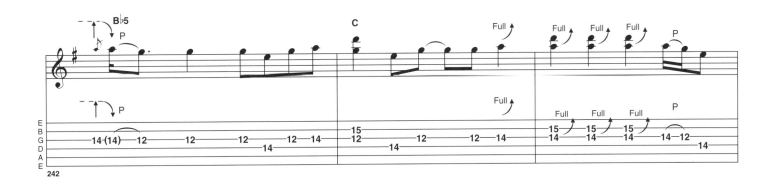

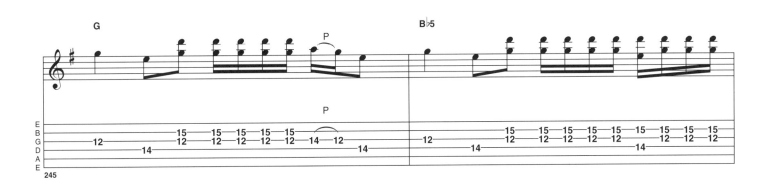

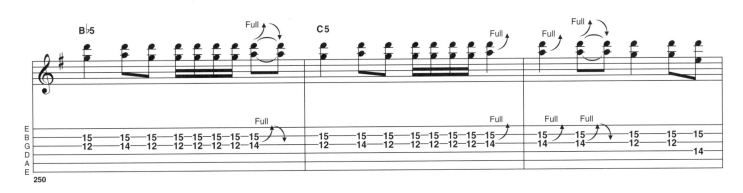

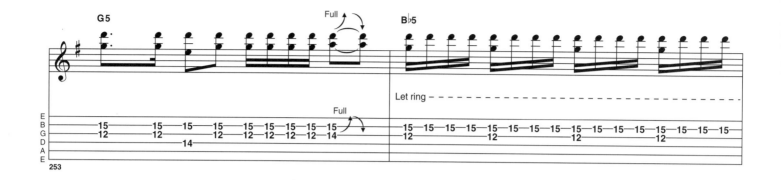

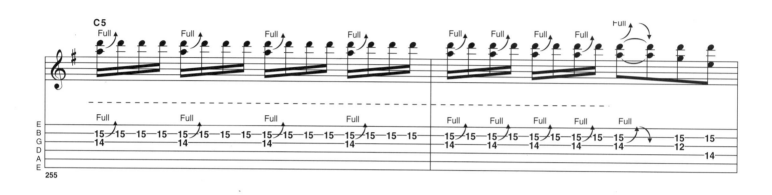

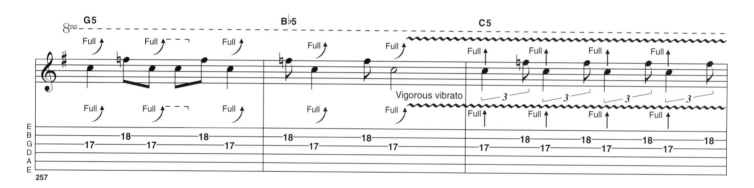

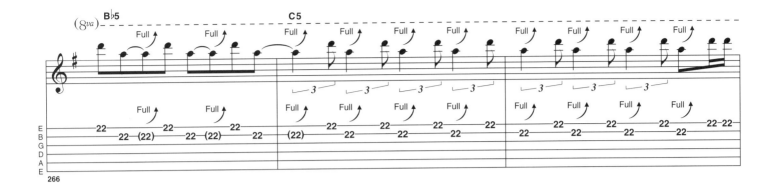

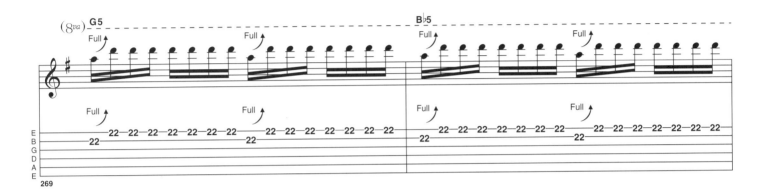

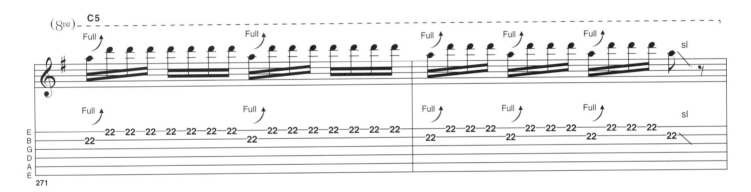

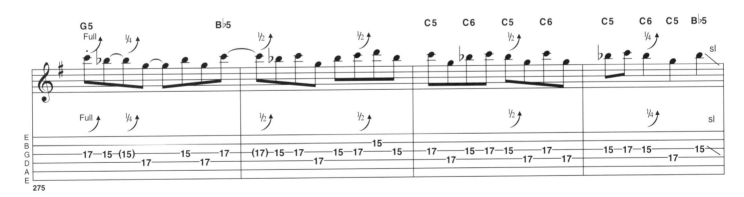

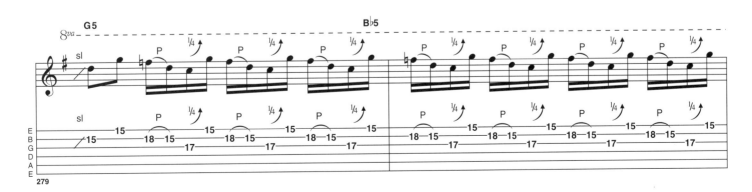

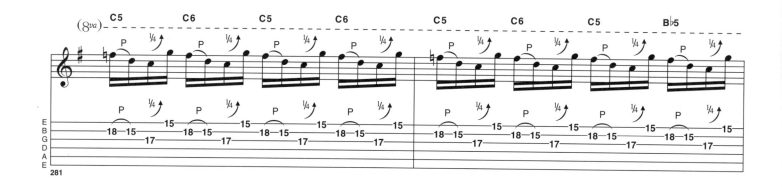

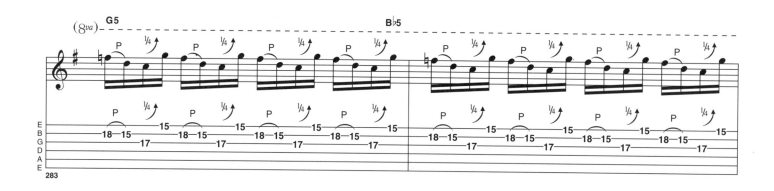

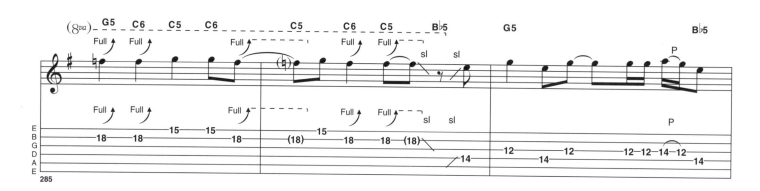

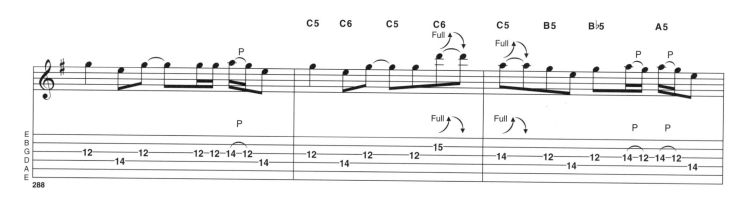

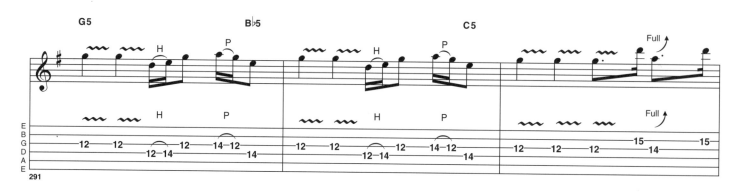

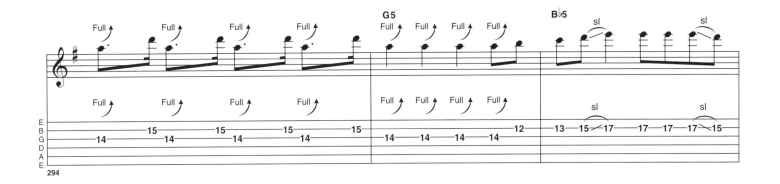

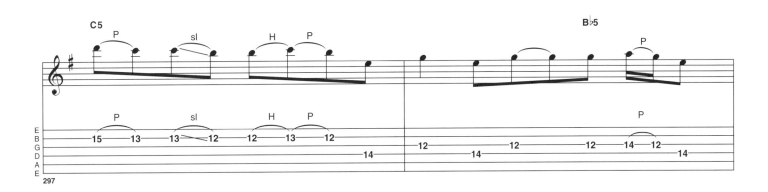

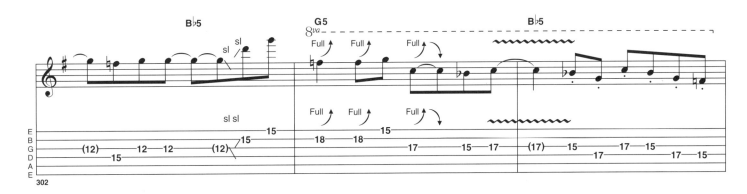

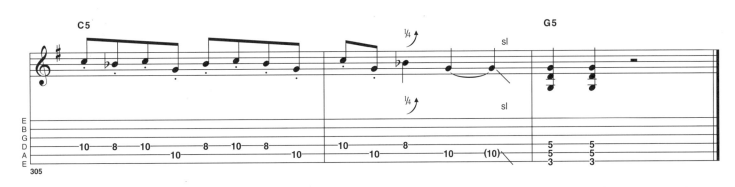

Sweet Home Alabama

LYNYRD SKYNYRD

Words & Music by
Ronnie Van Zant, Ed King & Gary Rossington

3. In Bir-ming-ham— they loved the go - vernor (Boo hoo

hoo) now we all did— what we could do.— Now Wa-ter-gate— does not

bo - ther me does your con-science bo - ther you?— tell the truth.

CHORUS

Sweet— home A - la - ba - ma

(include slide to D at beginning of bar on 1st repeat)

where   the   skies   are   so blue.___
Lord   I'm coming   home___ to   you.

SOLO 2

slow even bend

w/bar

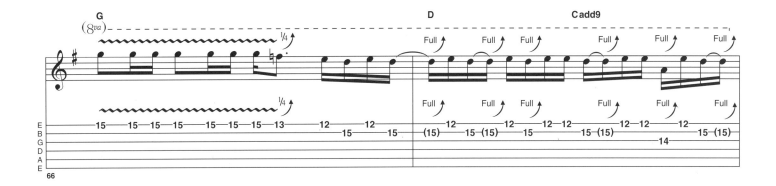

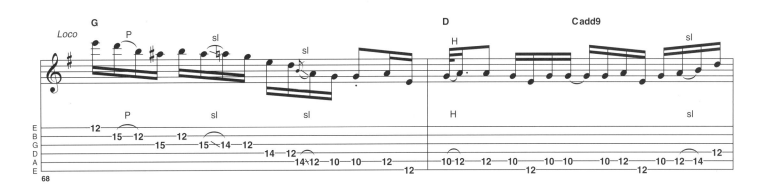

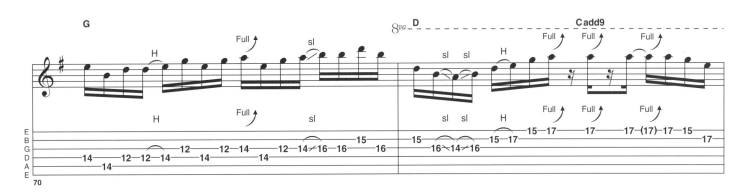

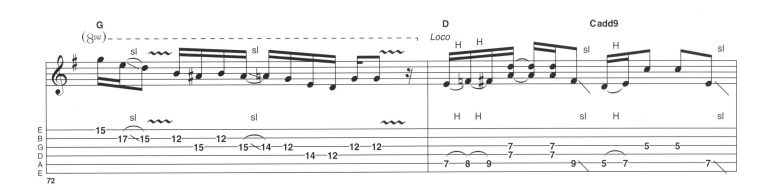

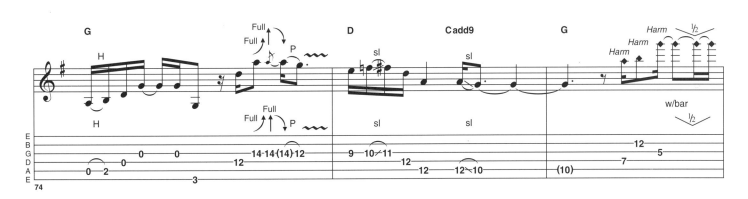

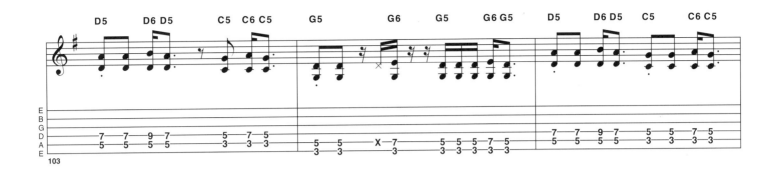

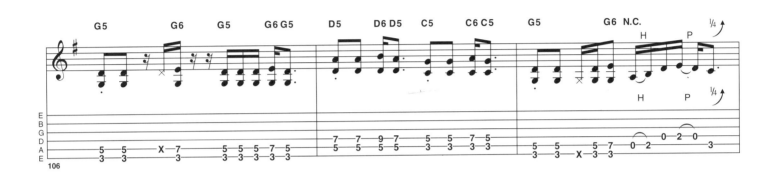

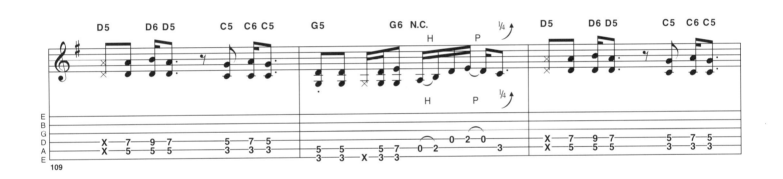

End of original fade out

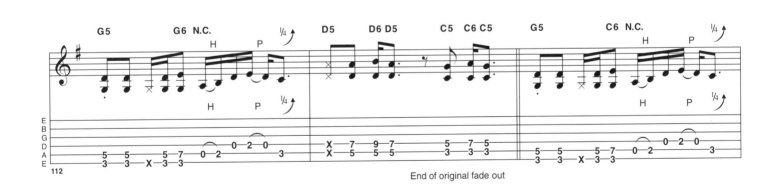

Rocky Mountain Way

JOE WALSH

Words & Music by
Joe Walsh, Joe Vitale,
Kenny Passarelli & Rocke Grace

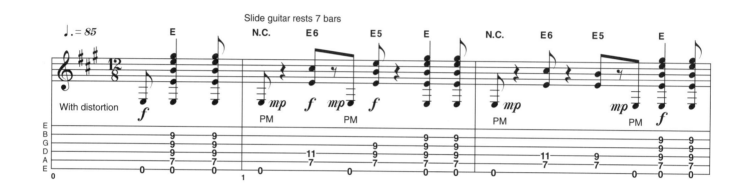

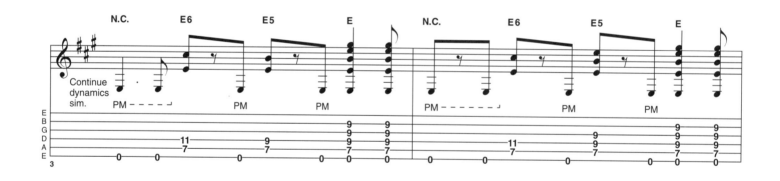

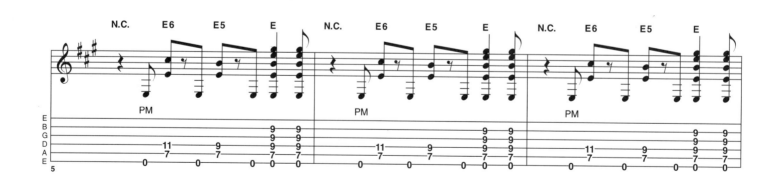

1. Spent the last year, Ro - cky Moun - tain way.— Coul - dn't get— much high-
tellin' us this and he's tellin' us that. Changes it ev'ry day. Says it doesn't mat -

even gliss
* Do not play on repeat

- er. Out to pas - ture, think it's safe— to say.
- ter. Bases are loaded and Casey's at bat, playin' it play by play.

Time to o - pen fire.— And we
Time to change the bat - - - ter.

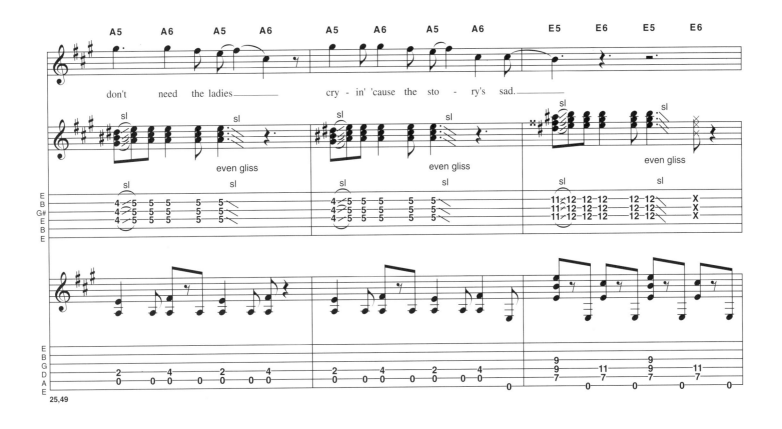

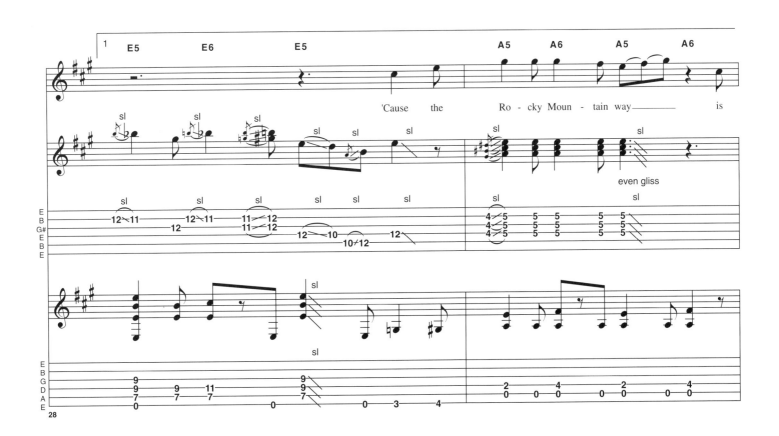

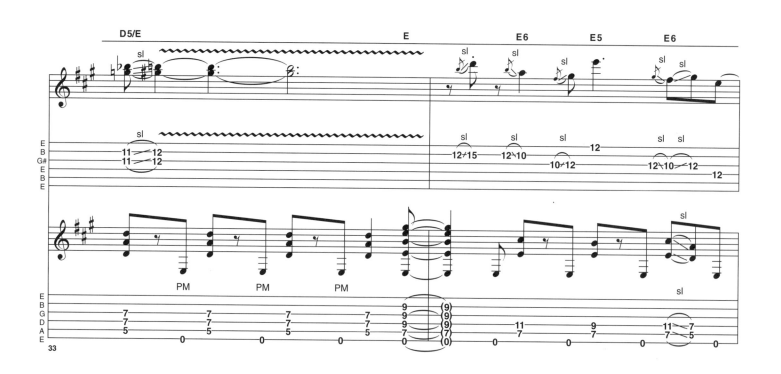

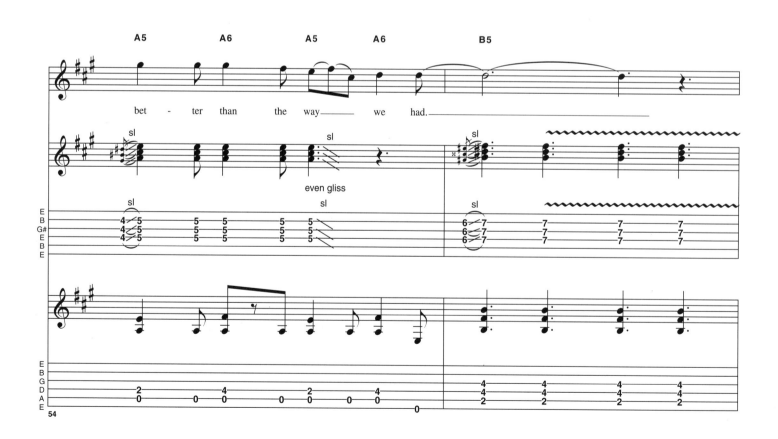

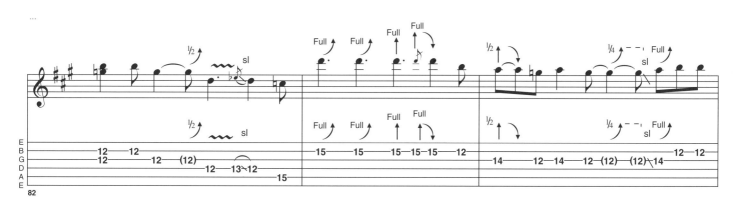

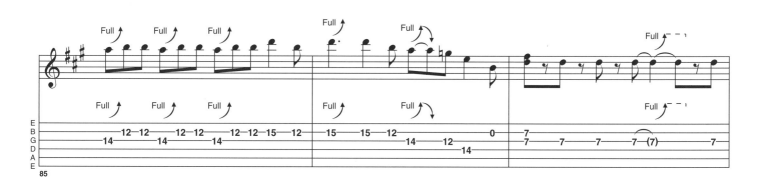

83

More Than A Feeling

BOSTON

Words & Music by
Tom Scholz

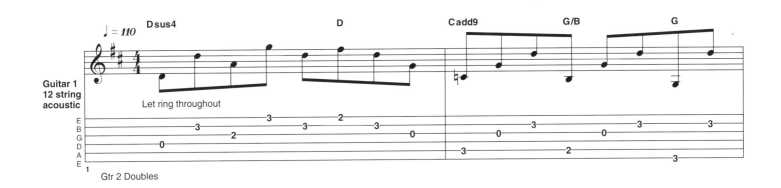

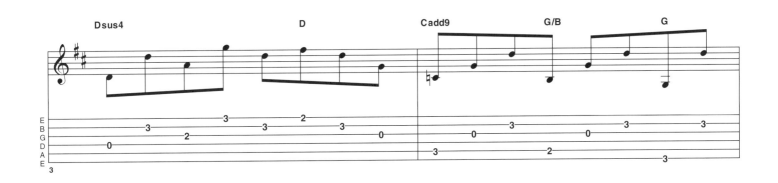

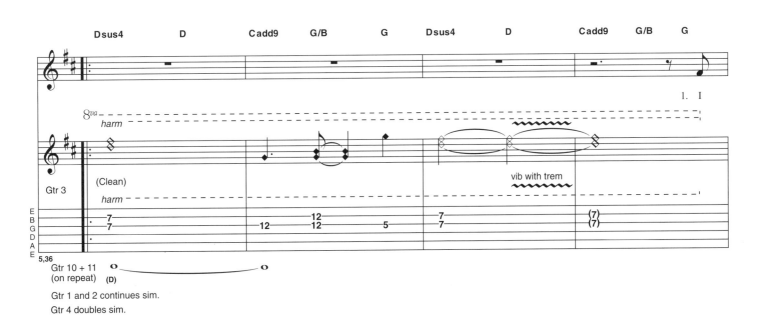

Gtr 1 + 2 continue

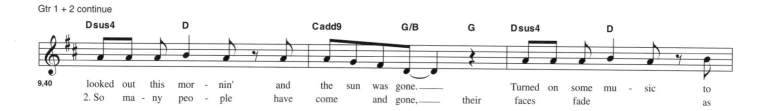

looked out this mor - nin' and the sun was gone._____ Turned on some mu - sic to
2. So ma - ny peo - ple have come and gone,_____ their faces fade as

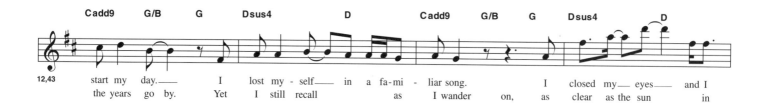

start my day._____ I lost my - self_____ in a fa - mi - liar song. I closed my_____ eyes_____ and I
the years go by. Yet I still recall as I wander on, as clear as the sun in

slipped a - way._____
the summer_____ sky._____

Gtr 1

Gtr 2 doubles Gtr 1

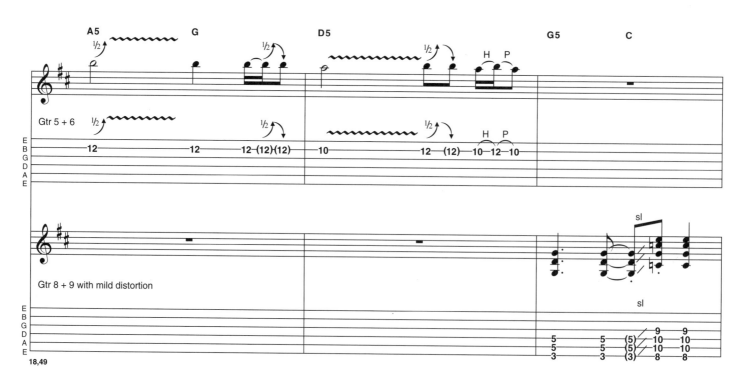

Gtr 5 + 6

Gtr 8 + 9 with mild distortion

90

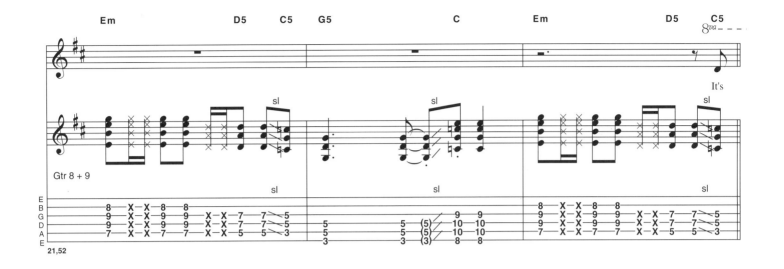

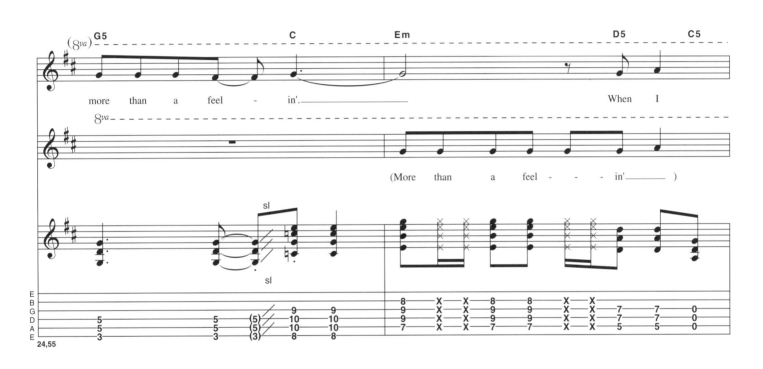

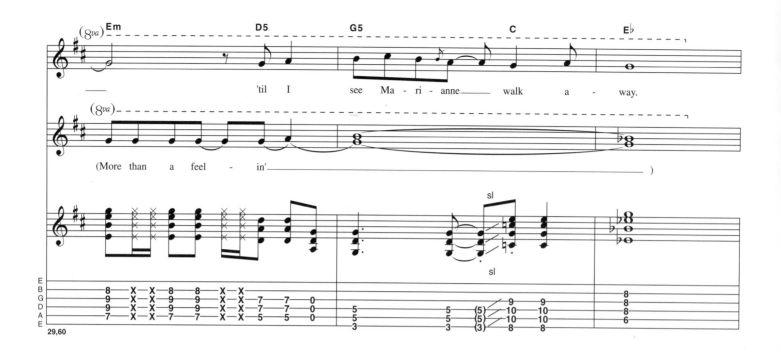

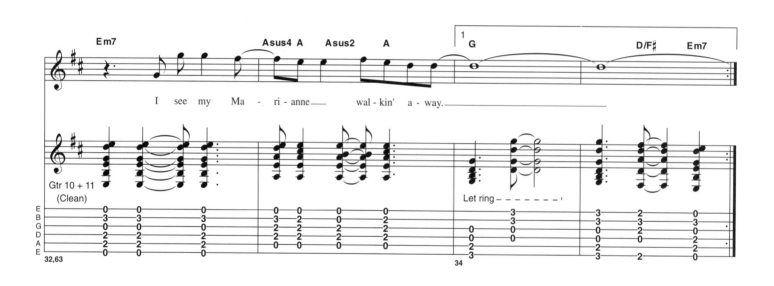

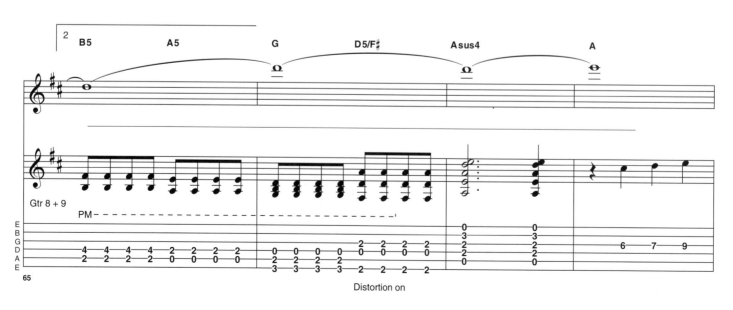

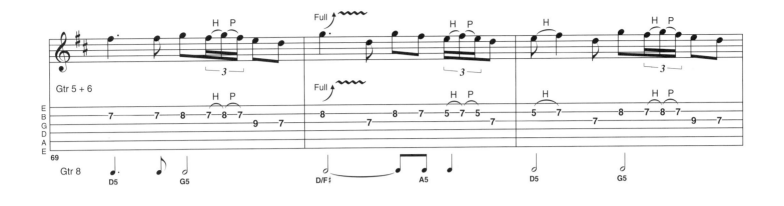

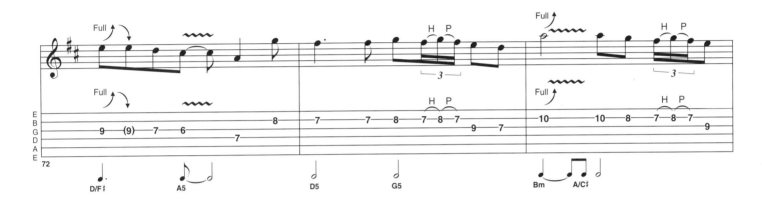

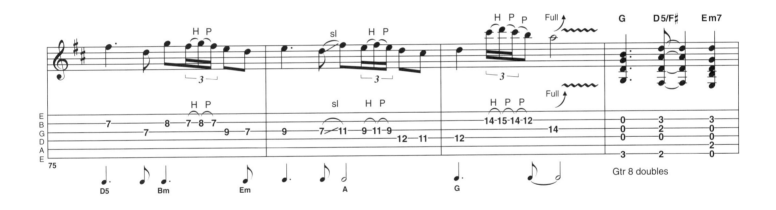

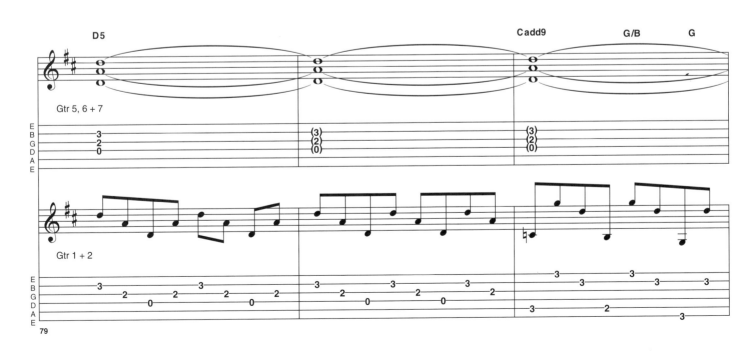

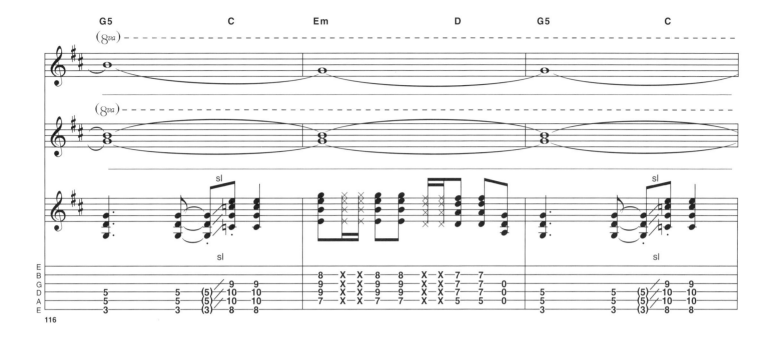

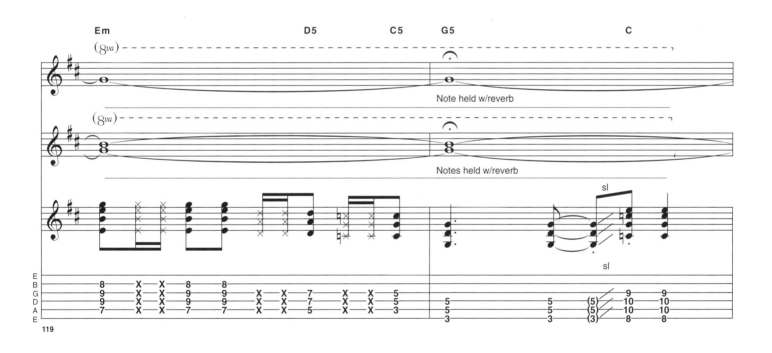

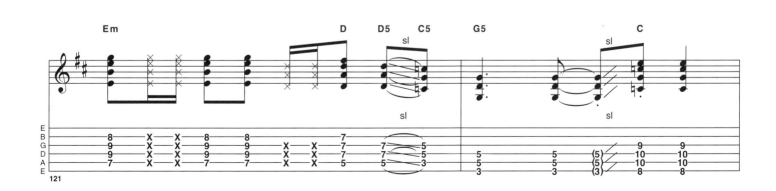

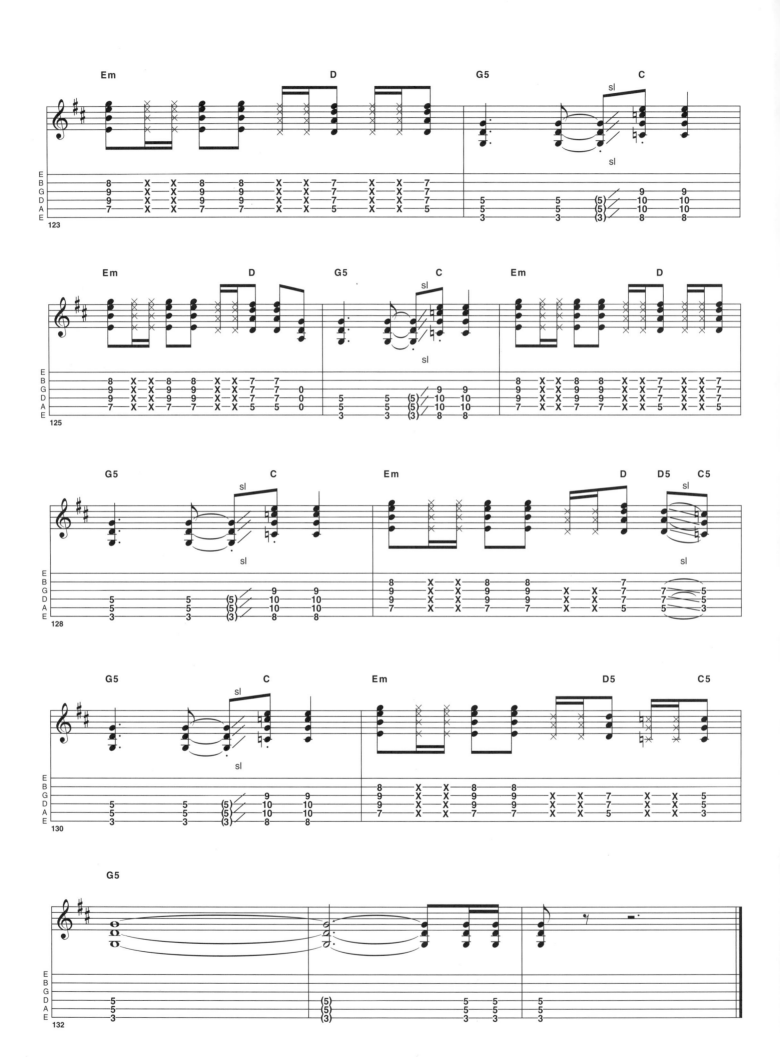

Born To Be Wild

STEPPENWOLF

Words & Music by Mars Bonfire

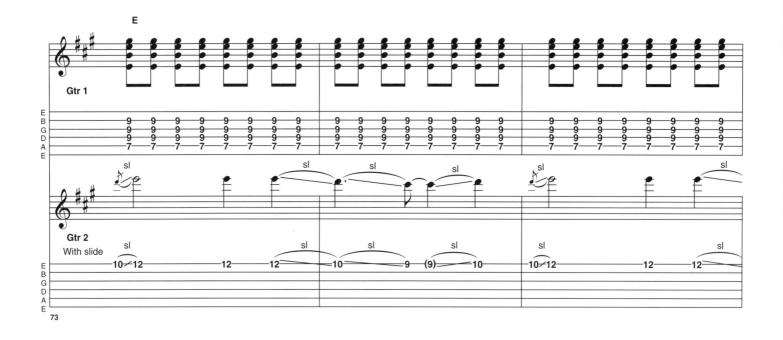

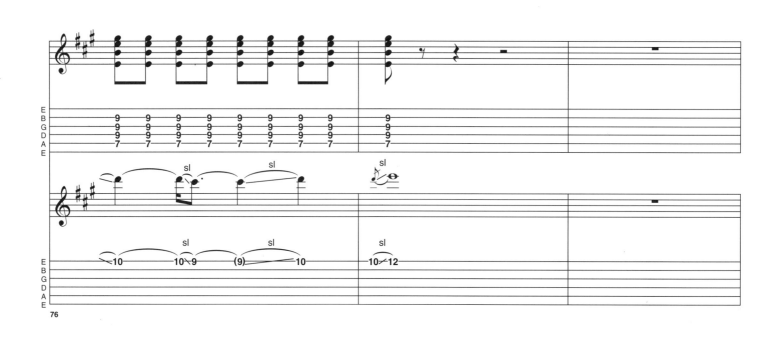

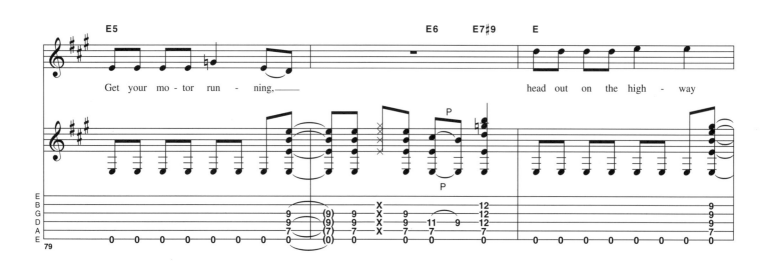

Get your mo - tor run - ning, head out on the high - way

Won't Get Fooled Again

THE WHO

Words & Music by
Pete Townshend

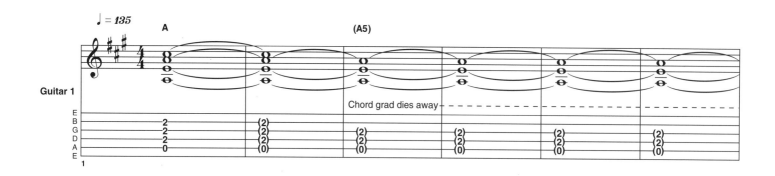

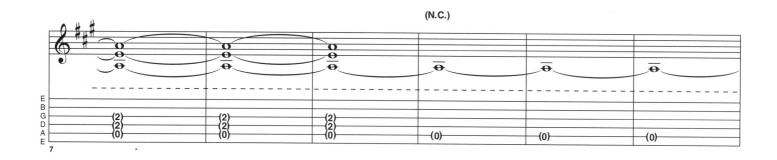

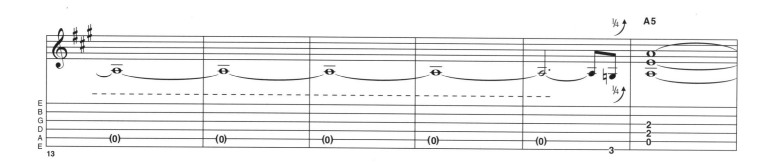

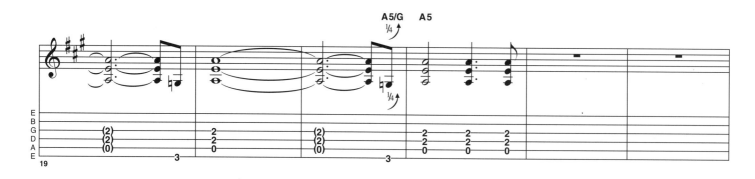

CHORUS

I'll tip my hat to the new cons-ti-tu-tion   take a bow____ for the

new re-vo-lu-tion   smile and grin____ at the change all a-round.   Pick up my gui-tar   and play.

Just like yes-ter-day.   Then I'll   get on   my knees and

pray.   We   don't   get fooled____ a-gain.____

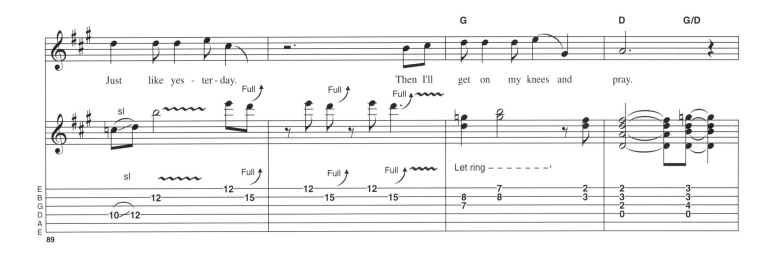

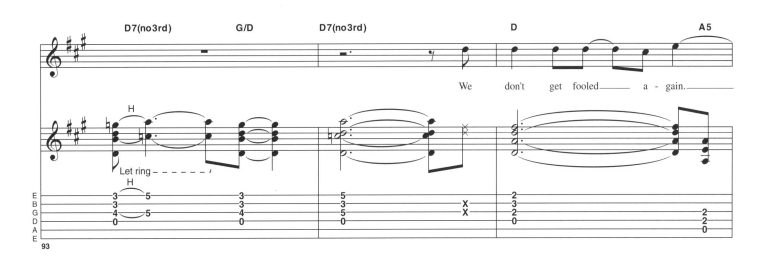

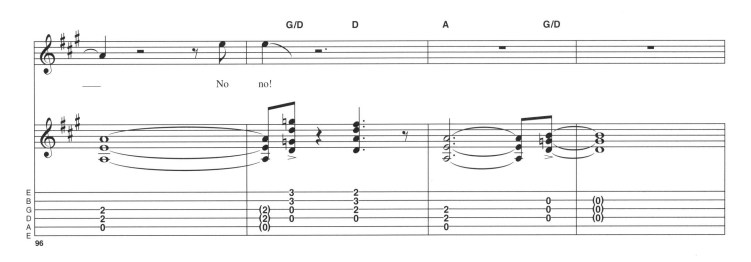

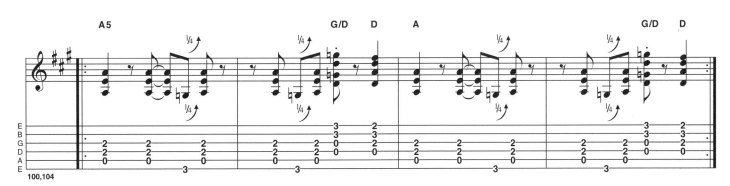

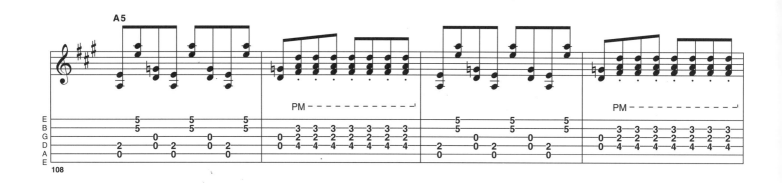

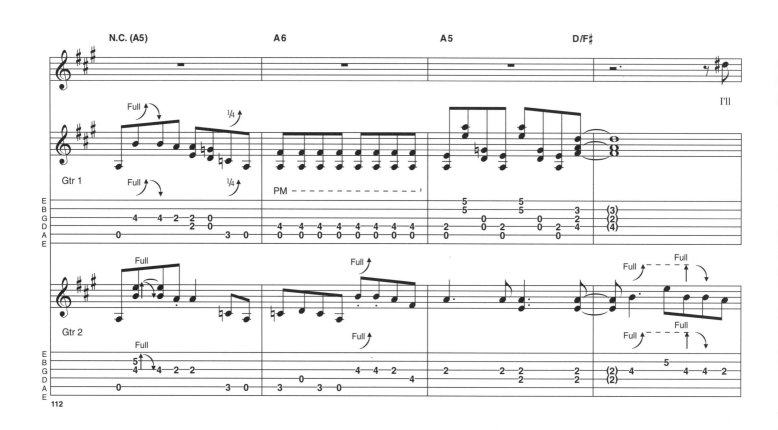

move my-self and my fami-ly a-side. ____ If we hap-pen to be

Gtr 2 doubles

GUITAR SOLO

116

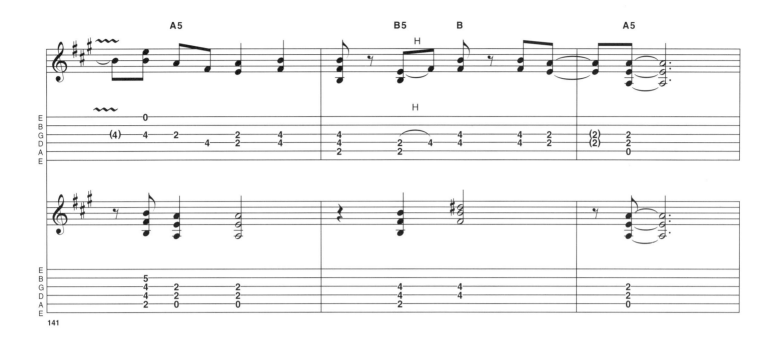

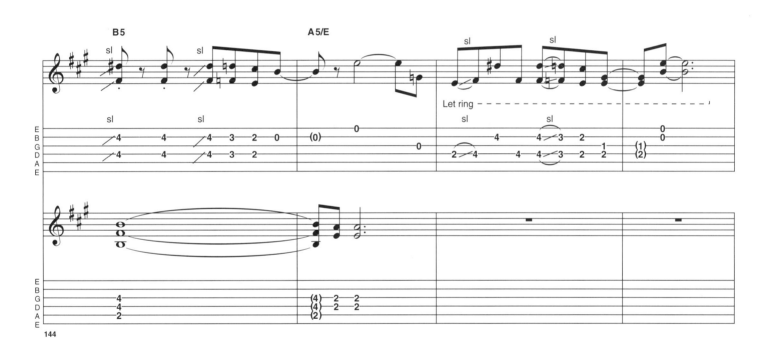

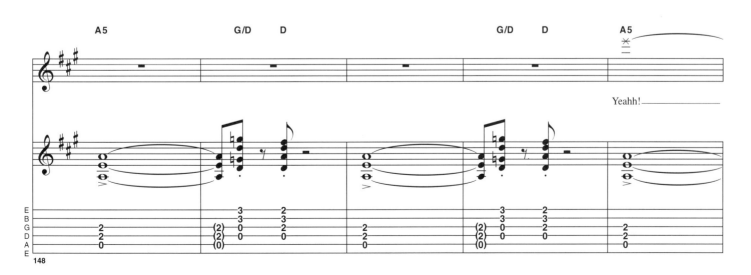

CHORUS

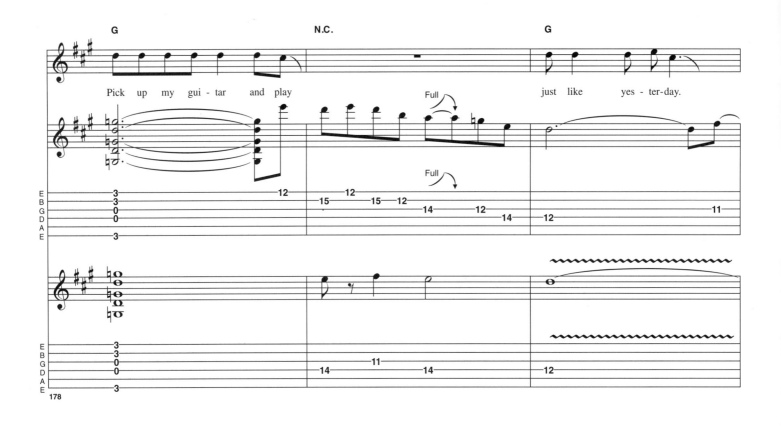

Pick up my gui- tar and play   just like yes - ter-day.

178

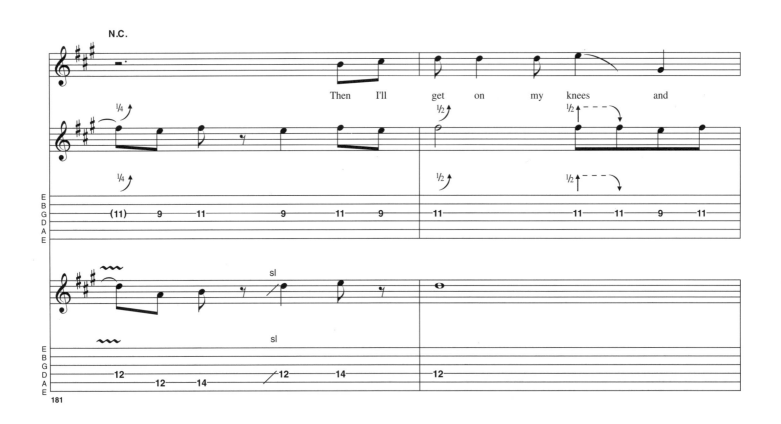

Then I'll get on my knees and

181

JAM JAM JAM

with the biggest rock stars of all time
Collect the whole series...

AC/DC

LET THERE BE ROCK
HELL AIN'T A BAD PLACE
 TO BE
WHOLE LOTTA ROSIE
HELLS BELLS
BACK IN BLACK
FOR THOSE ABOUT TO
 ROCK
SIN CITY
HIGHWAY TO HELL
Order No. AM961708

BRYAN ADAMS

SUMMER OF '69
RUN TO YOU
HEAVEN
IT'S ONLY LOVE
THE ONLY THING THAT
 LOOKS GOOD ON ME IS YOU
CAN'T STOP THIS THING WE
 STARTED
SOMEBODY
KIDS WANNA ROCK
Order No. AM966009

THE BEATLES

GET BACK
PAPERBACK WRITER
DAY TRIPPER
I FEEL FINE
I SAW HER STANDING
 THERE
WHILE MY GUITAR GENTLY
 WEEPS
LET IT BE
BACK IN THE USSR
Order No. NO90680

THE BEATLES VOL.2

WE CAN WORK IT OUT
TICKET TO RIDE
AND I LOVE HER
NORWEGIAN WOOD
A HARD DAY'S NIGHT
YESTERDAY
YOU'VE GOT TO HIDE
 YOUR LOVE AWAY
HERE COMES THE SUN
Order No. NO90685

BON JOVI

LIVING ON A PRAYER
WANTED DEAD OR ALIVE
YOU GIVE LOVE A BAD
 NAME
DRY COUNTRY
IN THESE ARMS TONIGHT
BLAZE OF GLORY
KEEP THE FAITH
BAD MEDICINE
Order No. AM953931

ERIC CLAPTON

LAYLA
WONDERFUL TONIGHT
HIDEAWAY
WHITE ROOM
CROSSROADS
COCAINE
TEARS IN HEAVEN
BAD LOVE
Order No. AM953920

DIRE STRAITS

BROTHERS IN ARMS
SULTANS OF SWING
ROMEO AND JULIET
PRIVATE INVESTIGATIONS
TELEGRAPH ROAD
MONEY FOR NOTHING
WALK OF LIFE
TUNNEL OF LOVE
Order No. DG70818

BUDDY HOLLY

THAT'LL BE THE DAY
HEARTBEAT
NOT FADE AWAY
PEGGY SUE
RAVE ON
EVERY DAY
OH BOY
IT DOESN'T MATTER
 ANYMORE
Order No. AM959827

PAUL KOSSOFF

ALL RIGHT NOW
THE HUNTER
MR BIG
WISHING WELL
FIRE AND WATER
MY BROTHER JAKE
THE STEALER
I'M A MOVER
Order No. AM959838

THIN LIZZY

DON'T BELIEVE IN A WOR
WAITING FOR AN ALIBI
STILL IN LOVE WITH YOU
THE BOYS ARE BACK IN
 TOWN
WHISKY IN THE JAR
JAILBREAK
ROSALIE
EMERALD
Order No. AM949509

70s ROCK

BLACK SABBATH: PARANO
ERIC CLAPTON: LAYLA
LYNYRD SKYNYRD:
 FREE BIRD
 SWEET HOME ALABAMA
JOE WALSH:
 ROCKY MOUNTAIN WAY
BOSTON:
 MORE THAN A FEELING
STEPPENWOLF:
 BORN TO BE WILD
THE WHO:
 WON'T GET FOOLED AGA
Order No. AM967428

90s ROCK

STEREOPHONICS:
 JUST LOOKING
 HURRY UP AND WAIT
OASIS:
 LIVE FOREVER
 WONDERWALL
OCEAN COLOUR SCENE:
 THE RIVERBOAT SONG
MANIC STREET PREACHERS
 DESIGN FOR LIFE
PAUL WELLER:
 CHANGING MAN
SEAHORSES:
 LOVE IS THE LAW
Order No. AM965987

play guitar with...

...the legends of rock - over 60 great book & CD titles to collect!

AC/DC
Includes:
back in black
highway to hell
whole lotta rosie
Order No. AM955900

the beatles
Includes:
day tripper
get back
yesterday
Order No. NO90665

the beatles Book 2
Includes:
eight days a week
please please me
ticket to ride
Order No. NO90667

the beatles Book 3
Includes:
here comes the sun
revolution
while my guitar gently weeps
Order No. NO90689

chuck berry
Includes:
around and around
johnny b. goode
no particular place to go
Order No. AM943789

black sabbath
Includes:
iron man
paranoid
war pigs
Order No. AM955911

blur
Includes:
country house
girls and boys
parklife
Order No. AM935320

bon jovi
Includes:
livin' on a prayer
wanted dead or alive
you give love a bad name
Order No. AM92558

eric clapton
Includes:
layla
sunshine of your love
tears in heaven
Order No. AM950862

phil collins
Includes:
another day in paradise
don't lose my number
one more night
Order No. AM928147

the corrs
Includes:
forgiven, not forgotten
so young
what can i do
Order No. AM960971

the cranberries
Includes:
hollywood
ridiculous thoughts
zombie
Order No. AM941699

dire straits
Includes:
money for nothing
romeo and juliet
sultans of swing
Order No. DG70735

free
Includes:
all right now
fire and water
wishing well
Order No. AM960960

david gilmour
Includes:
learning to fly
on the turning away
take it back
Order No.AM954602

buddy holly
Includes:
rave on
words of love
peggy sue
Order No. AM943734

john lee hooker
Includes:
boom boom
the healer
i'm in the mood
Order No. AM951885

b.b. king
Includes:
every day i have the blues
rock me baby
the thrill is gone
Order No. AM951874

the kinks
Includes:
all day and all of the night
waterloo sunset
you really got me
Order No. AM951863

kula shaker
Includes:
govinda
hey dude
hush
Order No. AM943767

john lennon
Includes:
cold turkey
happy xmas (war is over)
woman
Order No. AM943756

bob marley
Includes:
i shot the sheriff
jamming
no woman, no cry
Order No. AM937739

metallica
Includes:
enter sandman
fade to black
the unforgiven
Order No. AM92559

metallica Book 2
Includes:
creeping death
seek and destroy
whiskey in the jar
Order No. AM955977

alanis morissette
Includes:
hand in my pocket
ironic
you oughta know
Order No. AM943723

oasis
Includes:
cigarettes & alcohol
morning glory
supersonic
Order No. AM935330

ocean colour scene
Includes:
the circle
the day we caught the train
the riverboat song
Order No. AM943712

elvis presley
Includes:
all shook up
blue suede shoes
hound dog
Order No. AM937090

pulp
Includes:
common people
disco 2000
sorted for e's & wizz
Order No. AM938124

the rolling stones
Includes:
brown sugar
(i can't get no) satisfaction
jumpin' jack flash
Order No. AM90247

stereophonics
Includes:
just looking
pick a part that's new
the bartender & the thief
Order No. AM960950

sting
Includes:
an englishman in new york
fields of gold
if you love somebody
 set them free
Order No. AM928092

the stone roses
Includes:
i am the resurrection
i wanna be adored
ten storey love song
Order No. AM943701

the stone roses Book 2
Includes:
fool's gold
love spreads
one love
Order No. AM955890

suede
Includes:
animal nitrate
electricity
we are the pigs
Order No. AM955955

paul weller
Includes:
the changingman
out of the sinking
wild wood
Order No. AM937827

the who
Includes:
i can see for miles
pinball wizard
substitute
Order No. AM955867

the 60's
Includes:
all along the watchtower
 (jimi hendrix)
born to be wild (steppenwolf)
not fade away (the rolling stones)
Order No. AM957748

the 70's
Includes:
all right now (free)
hotel california (the eagles)
live and let die (wings)
Order No. AM957759

the 80's
Includes:
addicted to love (robert palmer)
need you tonight (inxs)
where the streets have no
 name (u2)
Order No. AM957760

the 90's
Includes:
everything must go
 (manic street preachers)
love is the law (the seahorses)
wonderwall (oasis)
Order No. AM957770

blues legends
Includes:
crossroads blues (cream)
couldn't stand the weather
 (stevie ray vaughan)
killing floor (jimi hendrix)
Order No. AM958507

classic tracks
Includes:
every breath you take (the police)
hey joe (jimi hendrix)
ziggy stardust (david bowie)
Order No. AM961004

pop anthems
Includes:
angels (robbie williams)
road rage (catatonia)
what can i do (the corrs)
Order No. AM960982

the metal album
Includes:
fade to black (metallica)
live and let die (guns n' roses)
love bites (def leppard)
Order No. AM954426

the gold book
Includes:
johnny b. goode (chuck berry)
layla (eric clapton)
sultans of swing (dire straits)
Order No. AM951907

the platinum book
Includes:
a design for life (manic street
 preachers)
cigarettes & alcohol (oasis)
the riverboat song
 (ocean colour scene)
Order No. AM951918

...and many more!